# INSPIRE MATHS

# TEACHER'S GUIDE 1B

*Noogol*

*Googol*

*Koogol*

*Ooogol*

*Toogol*

*Zoogol*

Consultant and author
Dr Fong Ho Kheong

Authors
Chelvi Ramakrishnan and Bernice Lau Pui Wah

UK consultants
Carole Skinner, Simon d'Angelo and Elizabeth Gibbs

OXFORD
UNIVERSITY PRESS

© 2015 Marshall Cavendish Education Pte Ltd

**Published by Marshall Cavendish Education**
Times Centre, 1 New Industrial Road, Singapore 536196
Customer Service Hotline: (65) 6213 9444
Email: tmesales@mceducation.com
Website: www.mceducation.com

Distributed by
**Oxford University Press**
Great Clarendon Street, Oxford,
OX2 6DP, United Kingdom
www.oxfordprimary.co.uk
www.oxfordowl.co.uk

First published 2015
Reprinted 2015, 2016 (twice), 2017

ISBN 978-981-01-3116-6

Printed in the United Kingdom

Acknowledgements
Written by Dr Fong Ho Kheong, Chelvi Ramakrishnan and Bernice Lau Pui Wah

UK consultants: Carole Skinner, Simon d'Angelo and Elizabeth Gibbs

Cover artwork by Daron Parton

The authors and publisher would like to thank all schools and individuals who helped to trial and review Inspire Maths resources.

# Contents

# The background to *Inspire Maths*

**A letter from Dr Fong Ho Kheong**

Dear Colleague,

I am both humbled and proud to see that my work has now been adapted for use in many countries. *My Pals are Here!*, the series from which *Inspire Maths* is adapted, has been translated into languages including Spanish, Indonesian, Dutch and Arabic, and the books are used by millions of children all over the world.

International surveys show that children taught with the series score higher than their peers in standardised tests, and also that it helps young children to become more confident with maths. The 2012 PISA survey again placed Singapore's children at the top of international rankings for mathematics; the country also had the highest percentage of top achievers. In the USA, it was reported in 2013 that schools in the Fayette County, West Virginia who had adopted the programme had made impressive progress in their mathematics results, including a 12 per cent improvement among third graders in one school and a 20 per cent improvement among fourth graders in another.

**Why does *Inspire Maths* work?** A major strength of *Inspire Maths* is its robust structure, based on best-practice principles and methods of teaching and learning mathematics, including the concrete-pictorial-abstract (CPA) and scaffolding approaches, and a systematic teaching pathway. This comprehensive pathway emphasises mastery – with continuous, active reinforcement of concepts to help children assimilate and accommodate their learning – followed by extension, challenging children to develop and practise the thinking skills that will enable them to become confident, critically aware and independent learners. The textbooks from which *Inspire Maths* is adapted have also been informed by continuous evaluation of their success in the classroom, through a process of school visits, classroom observation and programme review. Because of this, *Inspire Maths* gives you a proven framework for supporting children of all abilities to achieve success.

*Inspire Maths* is based on well-established constructivist ideas of learning, and the views of internationally-renowned educationalists including Jerome Bruner, Jean Piaget, Lev Vygotsky, Richard Skemp and David Ausubel. Constructivism underpins the programme's approach to learning mathematical concepts and skills through assimilation and accommodation, and their reinforcement through reflective activities such as journal writing and error correction. This perspective is also reflected in the programme's emphasis on mastery learning and building children's confidence.

More particularly, Bruner's three modes of representation are mirrored by the concrete–pictorial–abstract learning progression which is central to *Inspire Maths*. Bruner's ideas parallel Piaget's stages of development; essentially, children's understanding of mathematical concepts depends on their stage of development. Learning in the early stages is achieved through concrete representation. Then, when ready, children can move on to pictorial representations – such as the bar model – which in turn provide them with a bridge to the abstract stage, and a flexible, fully independent understanding of the abstract, symbolic language of maths. Though it cannot be used to tackle every problem, the bar model has a particularly significant role in helping children at the concrete and semi-concrete operational stage (Piaget's developmental theory) to approach and solve problems successfully.

Skemp's ideas about instrumental and relational understanding are also an important part of the pedagogy underpinning *Inspire Maths*. Skemp suggests that learning mathematics by relating ideas to each other (relational understanding) is more meaningful, and therefore more effective, than memorising facts and procedures (instrumental understanding). Building on these ideas, *Inspire Maths* is designed to develop children's lasting and profound mathematical understanding which they will continue to extend and apply.

I would like to congratulate the UK schools and teachers who have made the choice to use *Inspire Maths*. I am confident that your children will experience similar success to that seen in other countries who have adopted this approach.

*Dr Fong*

Dr Fong achieved a PhD in Mathematics Education from King's College London before teaching mathematics in the National Institute of Education, Nanyang Technological University, for over 24 years. He is currently a senior Mathematics Specialist with the Regional Centre for Education in Science and Mathematics (RECSAM) in Penang, Malaysia. He has published more than 100 journal articles, research reports, and primary and secondary mathematics books, and his research work includes diagnosing children with mathematical difficulties and teaching thinking skills to solve mathematical problems.

# What is *Inspire Maths?*

*Inspire Maths* is the UK edition of *My Pals are Here!*, the internationally renowned approach used to teach maths in Singapore, which was heavily influenced by the Cockroft report of 1982[1]. Singapore's Ministry of Education drew on leading international research on effective teaching and learning of mathematics to meet the challenge of raising primary mathematics attainment within Singapore's schools.

The approach to mathematics teaching and learning that was developed was further refined over subsequent decades and it is this approach that is central to *My Pals are Here!* Authored by Dr Fong Ho Kheong and first published in 2001, *My Pals are Here!* is used by almost 100% of State Primary schools and over 80% of Primary schools in Singapore.

Dr Fong's overarching aim in developing *My Pals are Here!* was to help all children understand and use mathematics confidently and competently, and to support non-specialist maths teachers to deliver this. The programme's success in achieving this aim is reflected in the high levels of mathematics attainment by Singapore's pupils, who are consistently ranked among the very top in international comparison studies such as PISA and TIMSS. It is also reflected in the results of schools outside Singapore that have adopted the series, for example, in the USA and South Africa.

*Inspire Maths* provides a highly scaffolded learning framework with problem solving at its heart. It is built on a focused, coherent and cumulative spiral curriculum that continuously builds and consolidates knowledge to reach deep understanding. The programme encourages extensive practice to develop fluency and mastery, so that every child – across all abilities – can succeed at mathematics.

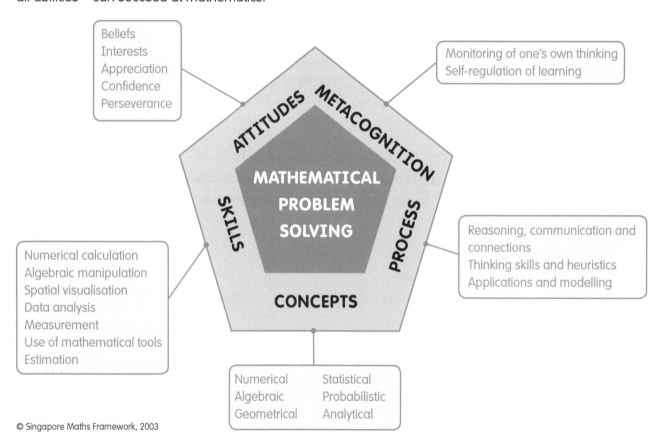

© Singapore Maths Framework, 2003

**The principles that underpin *Inspire Maths***

---

1    Mathematics Counts, Dr W.H.Cockroft, 1982

# The concrete-pictorial-abstract approach

*Inspire Maths* emphasises the development of critical thinking and problem solving skills, which help children make connections to develop deeper understanding. The powerful concrete–pictorial–abstract (CPA) approach, including the bar model method, is central to this.

Why is the CPA approach so powerful? From very early on in their school life, we expect children to use and understand numbers, which are abstract concepts. Many children struggle with this and so their first experiences of mathematics can be confusing, leaving them with no solid foundation to build on for later learning. The CPA approach helps children achieve secure number sense – that is, a sense of what numbers really represent and how to use them mathematically. This is done through a series of carefully structured representations – first using physical objects (concrete), then diagrams or pictures (pictorial), and ultimately using representations such as numerals (abstract).

In the example below from *Inspire Maths* Pupil Textbook IA, children are exploring order and pattern. Using the CPA approach, they explore with interlocking cubes, then using a number track, and finally through words, written symbols and calculations.

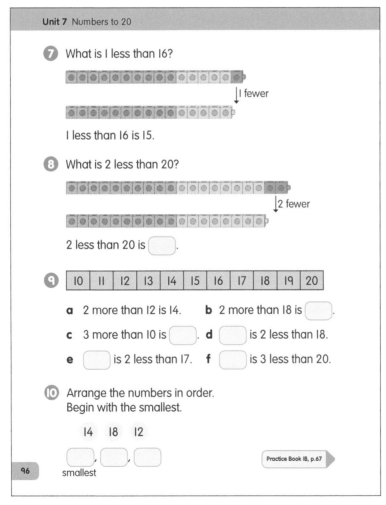

*Inspire Maths* **Pupil Textbook IA, page 96**

# The bar model

The bar model is a step-by-step method that helps children to understand and extract the information within a calculation or word problem. By drawing a bar model, children translate a calculation or word problem into a picture. The approach helps children process the information given in the problem, visualise the structure, make connections and solve the problem.

The bar model is first introduced in *Inspire Maths* 2. In the following activity, children explore addition and subtraction initially with concrete apparatus before moving on to using a pictorial representation – the bar model.

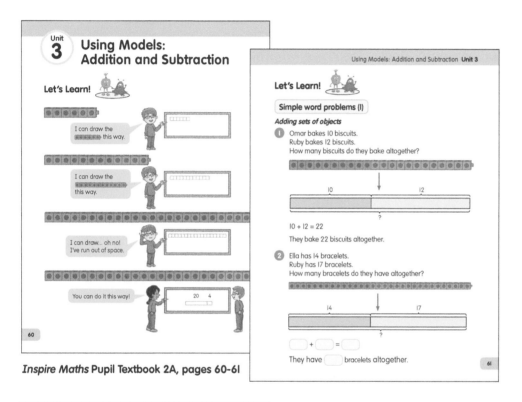

*Inspire Maths* Pupil Textbook 2A, pages 60-61

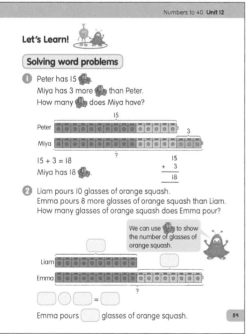

*Inspire Maths* Pupil Textbook 1B, page 59

In *Inspire Maths* 1, children are prepared for the introduction of the bar model by using concrete apparatus; for example, using interlocking cubes to compare the number of objects in two groups.

# Heuristics for problem solving

*Inspire Maths* helps children learn to use *heuristics* to solve problems. *Heuristics* refers to the different strategies that children can adopt to solve unfamiliar or non-routine problems. These strategies include drawing the bar model, pattern-spotting, using diagrams and estimating or 'guess and check'.

In this example from *Inspire Maths* Pupil Textbook IA, children spot patterns and relationships to solve the problems.

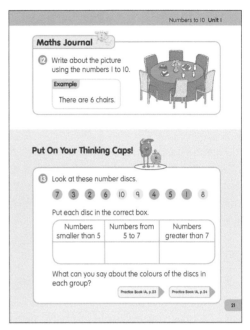

*Inspire Maths* **Pupil Textbook IA, page 21**

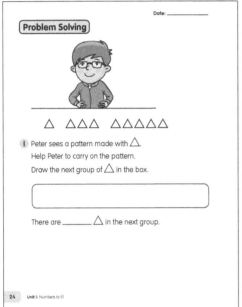

*Inspire Maths* **Practice Book IA, page 24**

The *Inspire Maths* Practice Books reinforce concepts introduced in the Pupil Textbooks and provide varied, frequent practice to develop fluency. As they practise, children begin to self-select the appropriate strategy for each problem, helping them to become confident problem solvers.

## Higher-order questioning

*Inspire Maths* is designed to stimulate thinking beyond the activities from the Pupil Textbooks. The activities should kick-start mathematically meaningful conversations through questioning, giving children opportunities to think mathematically, discover connections and be creative.

You can use written problems as a starting point for further questioning, for example, when presented with $7 + 4 = 11$ and an accompanying bar model, you might ask, 'What would happen if it was $11 - 4$? Or $11 - 7$? What about $7 + 4$ or $4 + 7$?' Then take it further: 'What would the bar model look like if it was $8 + 4$?'

Modelling higher-order questioning at every opportunity will encourage children to use this strategy to explore and solve problems for themselves.

# Making use of variation

Research shows that mathematical and perceptual variation deepens understanding as it constantly challenges children to develop their existing understanding by looking at questions from different perspectives and adapting to new situations. The numbers and problems in *Inspire Maths* activities have been specifically selected on this basis to challenge children as the questions progress and lead them towards mastery.

## Mathematical variation

With mathematical variation, the mathematical concept, for example addition, stays the same but the mathematics (and what children physically 'do') varies. For example, children may look at addition *without* regrouping or *with* regrouping. The variation challenges children to use their mathematical skills flexibly to suit the situation, deepening understanding.

## Perceptual variation

With perceptual variation, the mathematical concept is the same throughout the sequence of questions but is presented in different ways. This activity from *Inspire Maths* Pupil Textbook IA presents different ways of perceiving number bonds and encourages children to look for connections between the questions. For example, between questions I and 2, the total number of beads increases by two, and the number of beads visible under one cup increases by one, so the number of beads hidden under the second cup will increase by one.

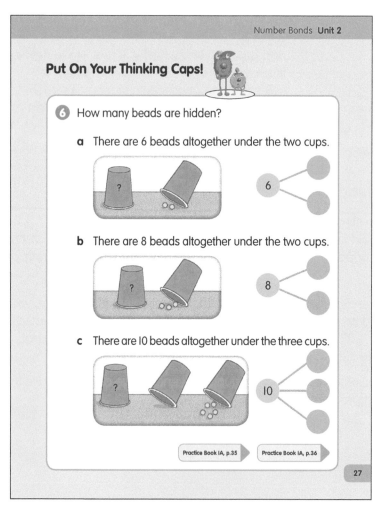

*Inspire Maths* Pupil Textbook IA, page 27

# The *Inspire Maths* teaching pathway

*Inspire Maths* is a programme that teaches to mastery. It is built on a cumulative spiral curriculum, focusing on core topics to build deep understanding. The *Inspire Maths* teaching pathway scaffolds in-depth learning of key mathematical concepts through the development of problem-solving and critical thinking skills, and extensive opportunities for practice.

## Pupil Textbooks to scaffold new learning

*Inspire Maths* Pupil Textbooks present new learning clearly and consistently, providing a highly scaffolded framework to support all children. Mathematical concepts are presented visually, with specific and structured activities, to build firm foundations. There are two Pupil Textbooks for each level.

### *Let's Learn!* to build firm foundations

Carefully scaffolded learning through *Let's Learn!* activities in the *Inspire Maths* Pupil Textbooks promotes deep mathematical understanding through:

- clearly presented pages to illustrate how the CPA approach can be used to build firm foundations

- careful questioning to support the use of concrete apparatus

- opportunities for higher-order questioning (see page ix) to help children become confident and competent problem solvers

- opportunities to assess each child's understanding and prior knowledge through observing their use of concrete apparatus and how they approach the activity

- use of mathematical talk to explore and develop reasoning skills.

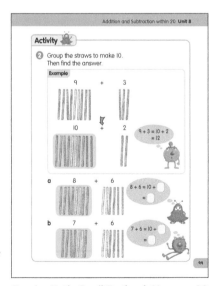

*Inspire Maths* Pupil Textbook IA, page 98

### Guided practice to develop deep understanding

After a concept has been introduced in *Let's Learn!*, guided practice develops the deep understanding required for mastery. Support and guide children as they work collaboratively in pairs or small groups through the guided practice activities indicated by empty coloured boxes in the Pupil Textbook.

Frequent opportunities for guided practice:

- help children develop deep understanding

- develop mathematical language and reasoning through collaborative work

- provide further opportunities to check children's understanding by observing their use of concrete apparatus and listening to their discussions

- help you to provide appropriate intervention – guiding those who need extra support and challenging those who are ready for the next step.

*Inspire Maths* Pupil Textbook IA, page 99

## Let's Explore! and Games to investigate and apply learning

Engaging games and investigative *Let's Explore!* activities in the *Inspire Maths* Pupil Textbooks encourage children to apply concepts they have been learning and provide an opportunity to assess their reasoning skills by observing how they approach the tasks.

Children work collaboratively in small groups or pairs:

- games reinforce skills, concepts and problem solving strategies leading to mastery

- *Let's Explore!* activities encourage children to investigate connections through mathematical reasoning

- meaningful discussion and conversation develop mathematical language.

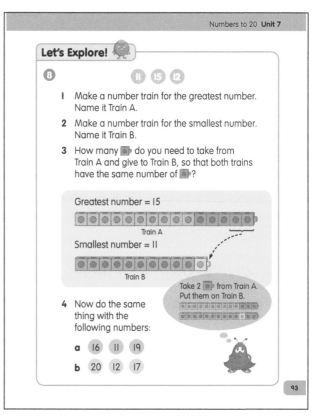

Inspire Maths Pupil Textbook IA, Page 93

## Maths Journal to reflect

The *Maths Journal* is where each child records their mathematical thinking and reflects on their learning. The typical Maths Journal would be a child's own exercise book or notebook – something that the child 'owns', can share with you, with parents or carers, and that builds up over time.

Children reflect on their learning through their Maths Journal:

- giving both the child and you a valuable assessment tool, showing progress over time

- providing opportunities for children to discuss their thinking with each other, parents or carers, and with you, helping to establish next steps and giving a sense of pride in their achievements.

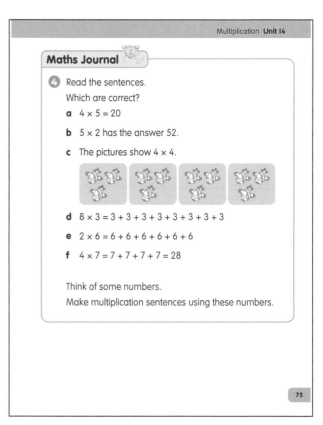

*Inspire Maths* Pupil Textbook IB, Page 75

## Put on Your Thinking Caps! to challenge

Each unit concludes with a *Put on Your Thinking Caps!* activity in the Pupil Textbook which challenges children to solve non-routine problems.

Challenging activities:

- ask children to draw on prior knowledge as well as newly learned concepts

- ask children to use problem solving strategies and critical thinking skills, for example sequencing or comparing

- provide valuable opportunities to assess whether children have developed a deep understanding of a concept by listening to their explanations of their mathematical thinking and looking at how they model the problem, for example using concrete apparatus and pictorial representations.

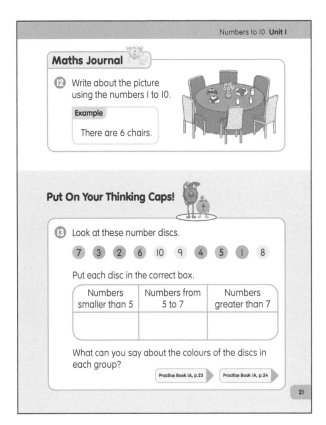

*Inspire Maths* Pupil Textbook IA, page 21

## Home Maths to encourage mathematical conversations

Home maths activities in the Pupil Textbooks are engaging, hands-on suggestions that parents and carers can use with children to explore maths further outside the classroom, for example through finding shapes in pictures and around the house.

Engaging home activities:

- help you to involve parents and carers in their child's mathematical learning

- help children to see maths in the world around them.

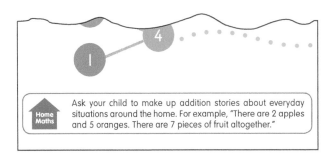

*Inspire Maths* Pupil Textbook IA, page 35

# Practice Books to develop fluency and consolidate

*Inspire Maths* Practice Books provide carefully structured questions to reinforce concepts introduced in the Pupil Textbooks and to provide varied, frequent practice. A wealth of activities develop fluency, build mathematical confidence and lead towards mastery. The Practice Books are also a valuable record of individual progress. There are four Practice Books for *Inspire Maths* 1-3 and two Practice Books for *Inspire Maths* 4-6.

Each Practice Book includes:

- **Challenging Practice** and **Problem Solving** activities to develop children's critical thinking skills

- **Reviews** after every two or three units, to reinforce learning

- **Revisions** that draw from a range of preceding topics, concepts and strands, for more complete consolidation.

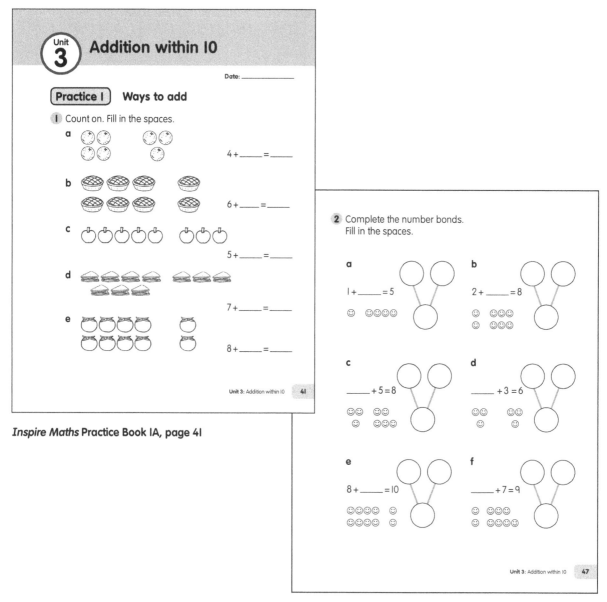

*Inspire Maths* Practice Book IA, page 41

*Inspire Maths* Practice Book IA, page 47

## Assessment Books to create a record of progress

*Inspire Maths* provides comprehensive Assessment Books with regular summative assessments to create a record of progress for each child, as well as giving children opportunities to reflect on their own learning. The wraparound assessment provided through the *Inspire Maths* teaching pathway in combination with the *Inspire Maths* Assessment Books enables rapid, appropriate intervention as soon as a child needs it, before they fall behind and when they are ready to be challenged. Topics and concepts are frequently revisited in the assessments, helping to build mastery.

There is one Assessment Book for each level, providing complete coverage of the key concepts across a year. Each assessment is divided into sections so you can easily break them down into appropriate chunks to suit your class. For the early levels, you may choose to assess in small groups, reading out the questions and scribing answers. Encourage children to use concrete apparatus when they need support to help them work through the questions.

There are three types of assessment within each Assessment Book:

1. **Main assessments:** The main assessments cover the key learning objectives from the preceding two or three units of the Pupil Textbooks. Through the main assessments, children are given opportunities to apply their learning in a variety of different contexts, helping you to quickly identify which children are ready to move on and which need further support. Children may self-mark to reflect on their progress.

2. **Check-ups:** There are four check-ups for each level which revisit the previous units, drawing on prior knowledge to encourage children to make connections and apply their learning to solve problems. These assessments give you valuable opportunities to check children's understanding through observing how they approach questions, use and interpret mathematical language and use heuristics.

3. **Challenging Problems:** These assessments make use of non-routine and unfamiliar questions to see how children use their repertoire of strategies to tackle more challenging problems. Use this as an opportunity to assess children's mathematical thinking, reasoning and problem solving skills by looking at their methods and how they approach the problem. They are particularly suitable for extension and assessing a child's level of mastery.

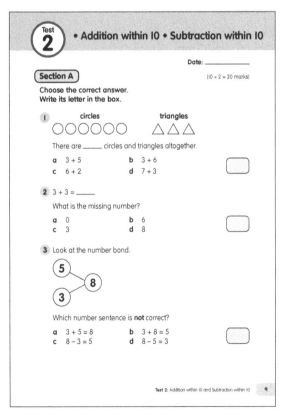

*Inspire Maths* Assessment Book 1, page 9

# Using the Teacher's Guide

There are two *Inspire Maths* Teacher's Guides for each level, one per Pupil Textbook. Each Teacher's Guide contains:

- information on how to get started
- long-term planning support
- medium-term planning support
- suggested teaching sequence for each pupil textbook page
- answers
- photocopiable activities.

**Key concepts** clearly outline the important ideas children will be introduced to within each unit.

**Learning objectives** clearly signal the aims of the unit, which are designed to help children develop their understanding of the unit's key concepts. Children are introduced to the learning objectives in the Pupil Textbook. The Practice Book provides opportunities to practise and consolidate for mastery.

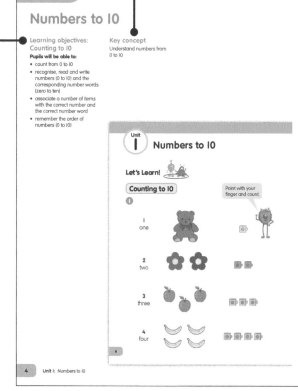

*Inspire Maths* Teacher's Guide 1A, pages 4-5

Ideas for **further practice activities** to develop fluency are outlined in every unit.

The **teaching sequence** provides clear step-by-step guidance towards meeting the learning objectives. It highlights problem solving strategies to focus on and support for meaningful mathematical conversation and making the best use of concrete apparatus.

Links to the Practice Books provide opportunities for **independent work** when children are ready, to develop fluency and lead towards mastery.

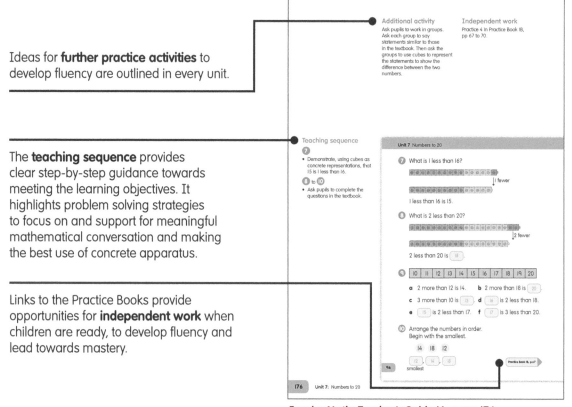

*Inspire Maths* Teacher's Guide 1A, page 176

**Equipment** needed for each Pupil Textbook page is listed to help you prepare for the activities.

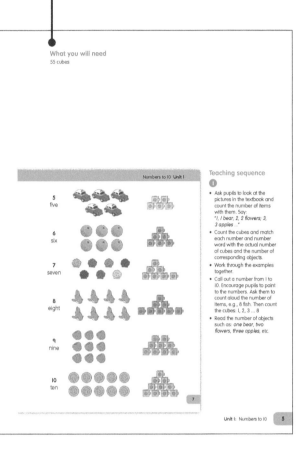

**Key thinking skills and problem solving strategies** to look for and encourage are clearly highlighted, helping you to make meaningful assessments of children's understanding.

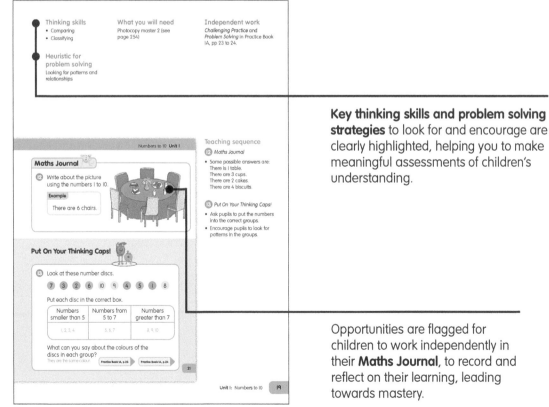

Opportunities are flagged for children to work independently in their **Maths Journal**, to record and reflect on their learning, leading towards mastery.

*Inspire Maths* Teacher's Guide 1A, page 19

# Long-term planning

| Unit title | Key concepts |
|---|---|
| **I Numbers to I0** | |
| Counting to I0 | • Understand numbers from 0 to I0 |
| Compare | • Two sets of objects can be compared using the method of one-to-one correspondence<br>• The number of objects can be the same as, smaller than or greater than another set of objects |
| Order and pattern | • A sequence of objects and numbers can form a pattern |
| **2 Number Bonds** | |
| Making number bonds | • Adding two or more numbers gives another number |
| **Practice Book – Review I** | |
| **Assessment Book – Test I** | |
| **3 Addition within I0** | |
| Ways to add | • Adding is associated with the 'part-whole' and 'adding on' concepts |
| Making up addition stories | |
| Solving word problems | • Applying the 'part-whole' and 'adding on' concepts in addition |
| **4 Subtraction within I0** | |
| Ways to subtract | • Subtracting is associated with the 'part-whole' and 'taking away' concepts |
| Making up subtraction stories | |
| Solving word problems | • Applying the 'part-whole' and 'taking away' concepts in subtraction |
| Making a family of number sentences | • A family of number sentences can be written from a set of three related numbers |
| **Practice Book – Review 2** | |
| **Assessment Book – Test 2, Challenging Problems I, Check-up I** | |
| **5 Shapes and Patterns** | |
| Getting to know shapes | • A circle has no corners and no sides<br>• A square has 4 equal sides and 4 corners<br>• A triangle has 3 sides and 3 corners<br>• A rectangle has 4 sides (opposite sides are equal) and 4 corners |
| Making pictures from shapes | • Shapes such as circles, triangles, squares and rectangles can be used to make pictures |
| Seeing shapes in things around us | • When an object is viewed from different angles/sides, we can see different shapes. For example, the top view of a tin of soup is a circle |
| Getting to know patterns | • Patterns are formed by repeating a particular arrangement of shape, size and/or colour placed next to each other |
| Making more patterns | • Patterns can be formed by repeating a particular arrangement of objects placed next to each other |

| Unit title | Key concepts |
|---|---|
| **6 Ordinal numbers** | |
| Knowing ordinal numbers | • Ordinal numbers are for describing the position of something |
| Naming left and right positions | • Positions from the left and right can be named using ordinal numbers |
| **Practice Book – Review 3** | |
| **7 Numbers to 20** | |
| Counting to 20 | • Use one-to-one correspondence in counting |
| Place value | • Numbers to 20 can be represented as tens and ones in a place value chart |
| Compare | • Numbers to 20 can be compared using the terms 'greater than' and 'smaller than' as well as by arranging in ascending or descending order |
| Order and pattern | • Numbers can be arranged in order and made into a pattern |
| **Assessment Book – Test 3** | |
| **8 Addition and Subtraction within 20** | |
| Ways to add | • Two I-digit numbers can be added by using the 'make 10' strategy and the 'regrouping into tens and ones' strategy |
| Ways to subtract | • 2-digit numbers can be regrouped into tens and ones |
| Solving word problems | • Applying the 'part-whole', 'adding on' and 'taking away' concepts in addition and subtraction |
| **9 Length** | |
| Comparing two things | • The lengths of two objects can be compared using the terms 'tall/taller', 'long/longer', 'short/shorter' and 'high/higher' |
| Comparing more things | • The lengths of more than two objects can be compared using the terms 'tallest', 'longest', 'shortest' and 'highest' |
| Using a start line | • A common starting point makes comparison of lengths easier |
| Measuring things | • Length can be measured using objects as non-standard units |
| Finding lengths in units | • Length can be described using the term 'unit' instead of paper clips or lolly sticks |
| **Practice Book – Revision I** | |
| **Assessment Book – Test 4, Challenging Problems 2, Check-up 2** | |
| **I0 Mass** | |
| Comparing things | • Compare masses using a pan balance |
| Finding the masses of things | • Mass can be measured using objects as non-standard units |
| Finding mass in units | • Mass can be described using the term 'units' |
| **II Picture graphs** | |
| Simple picture graphs | • Data can be collected and organised into a horizontal or vertical picture graph for interpretation |
| More picture graphs | • Data can be collected and organised into a horizontal or vertical picture graph using symbols |
| **Assessment Book – Test 5** | |

| Unit title | Key concepts |
|---|---|
| **12 Numbers to 40** | |
| Counting to 40 | • Using one-to-one correspondence in counting<br>• 1 ten equals ten ones |
| Place value | • Numbers to 40 can be represented as tens and ones in a place value chart |
| Comparing, order and pattern | • Numbers to 40 can be compared using the terms 'greater than' / 'smaller than' and 'greatest' / 'smallest' as well as arranged in ascending or descending order |
| Simple addition | • 'Add on' and 'part-whole' concepts are used in adding numbers |
| More addition | • 'Add on' and 'part-whole' concepts are used in adding numbers<br>• Regrouping concept can be applied in addition |
| Simple subtraction | • The 'taking away' concept is used in subtraction |
| More subtraction | |
| Adding three numbers | • 'Add on' and 'making ten' concepts are used in adding three numbers<br>• The regrouping concept is also applied |
| Solving word problems | • The 'part-whole', 'taking away', 'adding on' and 'comparing' concepts are used to solve word problems involving addition and subtraction |
| **Practice Book – Review 4** | |
| **13 Mental calculations** | |
| Mental addition | • A 2-digit number can be conceptualised as tens and ones<br>• Adding is conceptualised as adding or putting parts together |
| Mental subtraction | • A 2-digit number can be conceptualised as tens and ones<br>• Subtracting is conceptualised as taking away from a whole |
| **14 Multiplication** | |
| Adding the same number | • Multiplication is conceptualised as repeated addition |
| Making multiplication stories | • Tell stories based on the multiplication concept and repeated addition |
| Solving word problems | • Applying the multiplication concept to solve word problems |
| **Practice Book – Review 5** | |
| **Assessment Book – Test 6, Challenging Problems 3, Check-up 3** | |
| **15 Division** | |
| Sharing equally | • Division is conceptualised as dividing a set of objects equally |
| Finding the numbers of groups | • Division is conceptualised as sharing a set of items equally into groups |
| **16 Time** | |
| Telling the time to the hour | • Time can be used to measure the duration of an event |
| Telling the time to the half hour | • Measuring half an hour using the term 'half past' |
| **Practice Book – Review 6** | |
| **Assessment Book – Test 7** | |

| Unit title | Key concepts |
|---|---|
| **17  Numbers to 100** | |
| Counting | • Using one-to-one correspondence in counting<br>• I ten is the same as 10 ones<br>• 10 tens is 100 |
| Place value | • Numbers to 100 can be represented as tens and ones in a place value chart |
| Comparing, order and pattern | • Numbers to 100 can be compared using the terms 'greater than' and 'smaller than'<br>• Numbers to 100 can be arranged in ascending or descending order |
| Simple addition | • The 'adding on' and 'part-whole' concepts are used in adding numbers |
| More addition | • The 'adding on' and 'part-whole' concepts are used in adding numbers<br>• The regrouping concept is applied in addition |
| Simple subtraction | • The 'taking away' concept is used in subtraction |
| More subtraction | |
| **18 Money (1)** | |
| Getting to know our money | • Coins and notes in pounds and pence can be used to pay for goods and services. |
| Exchanging money | • A coin or note of one denomination can be used as the equivalent of another set of coins or notes of a smaller denomination |
| Work out the amount of money | • The amount of money can be counted in pence (up to £1) and pounds (up to £100) |
| **19 Money (2)** | |
| Adding and subtracting in pence | • Addition and subtraction concepts in numbers are used in addition and subtraction of money |
| Adding and subtracting in pounds | |
| Solving word problems | • The 'part-whole', 'adding on', 'taking away' and 'comparing' concepts in addition and subtraction are used in solving word problems |
| **Practice Book – Revision 2** | |
| **Assessment Book – Test 8, Challenging Problems 4, Check-up 4** | |

| Week | Learning Objectives | Thinking Skills | Resources |
|---|---|---|---|
| 1 | **(1) Comparing things**<br><br>Pupils will be able to:<br>• use the terms 'heavy', 'heavier', 'light' and 'lighter' to compare the masses of objects on a pan balance<br>• use the phrase 'as heavy as' to compare the masses of objects on a pan balance for objects with the same mass<br>• understand that size does not always determine mass<br>• use the terms 'heaviest' and 'lightest' to compare the masses of three objects<br>• guess the heavier or lighter object and use the pan balance to check if the guess is accurate<br>• determine the heavier or lighter object using modelling clay as an intermediate object. | • Comparing<br>• Deduction | • Pupil Textbook 1B, pp 6 to 10<br>• Practice Book 1C, pp 5 to 10<br>• Teacher's Guide 1B, pp 4 to 8 |
| 1–2 | **(2) Finding the masses of things**<br><br>Pupils will be able to:<br>• use a non-standard object such as a marble to find the masses of objects<br>• compare objects using a non-standard object as a medium of measurement | • Comparing<br>• Deduction | • Pupil Textbook 1B, pp 11 to 12<br>• Practice Book 1C, pp 11 to 14<br>• Teacher's Guide 1B, pp 9 to 10 |

# Medium-term plan

| Week | Learning Objectives | Thinking Skills | Resources |
|---|---|---|---|
| 2 | *Let's Explore!*<br><br>Pupils will be able to:<br>• use a pan balance to compare the masses of three objects and state the heaviest or the lightest object<br>• arrange the masses of the objects in decreasing order | • Comparing<br>• Deduction | • Pupil Textbook IB, p 12<br>• Teacher's Guide IB, p 10 |
| 2 | **(3) Finding mass in units**<br><br>Pupils will be able to:<br>• find the masses of objects using non-standard units<br>• use the term 'units' in writing the masses of objects<br>• explain why there is a difference in using different objects as measuring units | • Comparing<br>• Deduction<br>• Induction | • Pupil Textbook IB, pp 13 to 16<br>• Practice Book IC, pp 15 to 18<br>• Teacher's Guide IB, pp 11 to 14 |
| 2 | *Put On Your Thinking Caps!*<br><br>Pupils will be able to use comparing and deduction when given a set of measurements to arrange masses in order. | • Comparing<br>• Deduction<br>• Sequencing<br><br>Heuristics for problem solving:<br>• Act it out<br>• Guess and check<br>• Simplify the problem | • Pupil Textbook IB, p 17<br>• Practice Book IC, pp 19 to 22<br>• Teacher's Guide IB, p 15 |

# Mass

## Learning objectives: Comparing things

**Pupils will be able to:**

- use the terms 'heavy', 'heavier', 'light' and 'lighter' to compare the masses of objects on a pan balance
- use the phrase 'as heavy as' to compare the masses of objects on a pan balance for objects with the same mass

- understand that size does not always determine mass
- use the terms 'heaviest' and 'lightest' to compare the masses of three objects
- guess the heavier or lighter object and use the pan balance to check if the guess is accurate
- determine the heavier or lighter object using modelling clay as an intermediate object

## Key concept

Compare masses using a pan balance

## What you will need

- A pan balance
- Common objects, e.g., rubbers, books, fruits, pencil cases, rulers, toys

## Note

This is on the relative masses and not on the absolute masses of objects.

## Teaching sequence

- Ask pupils what the terms 'heavy', 'light', 'heavier' and 'lighter' mean. Encourage them to explain how they would know which object is heavier when comparing two objects.
- Illustrate the meanings of 'heavy' and 'heavier' using these examples:
  (a) Show pupils 3 objects of different mass, e.g., a pencil, an apple and a book. Ask them which object they think is heavier. Choose a pupil to try lifting the objects. Point out to pupils that heavier objects require more strength to lift.
  (b) Look at the picture in **1**. Ask pupils how they are able to tell that the hippo is heavier (the scale is lower). Ask pupils to verbalise: "*The hippo is heavier than the lion.*"

- Illustrate the meanings of 'light' and 'lighter' using the following example:
  (a) Look at the picture in **2**. Ask pupils how they are able to tell that the feather is lighter (the scale is higher). Ask pupils to say: "*The toy car is light. The feather is lighter.*"
- Show this using the pan balance and some objects.

## Unit 10 Mass

Let's Learn!

### Comparing things

**1**

lion

This lion is **heavy**.

hippo

This hippo is **heavier**.

**2**

toy car

feather

This toy car is **light**.

This feather is **lighter**.

6

## Thinking skills
- Comparing
- Deduction

## What you will need
- A pan balance
- Common objects, e.g., rubbers, soft toys, marbles
- Modelling clay moulded into different shapes
- A small heavy ball and a large lighter ball, e.g., marble and plastic ball or beach ball

## Additional activities
- Select two objects and invite volunteers to guess which is heavier. Pick objects which have an obvious difference in size and a corresponding difference in mass. Ask pupils to hold the objects to guess which object is heavier or lighter.

  Ask pupils to use the pan balance to check if they are right.

  Tell pupils that when the pan balance is not level, one of the objects is heavier than the other. The lighter object is on the higher pan, whereas the heavier object is on the lower pan.

Encourage pupils to use the words 'heavy/heavier' and 'light/lighter'.

- Ask pupils to guess if a smaller object is always heavier than a bigger object.

  Show pupils the marble and the light plastic ball and encourage pupils to guess which is heavier. Demonstrate by placing the objects on the pan balance.

  Point out to pupils that judging mass by size can be misleading, as a smaller object can sometimes be heavier than a bigger one.

  Ask pupils to give examples of how a bigger object can be lighter than a smaller object, e.g., a bag of cotton wool and a small marble.

## Teaching sequence
**3**

- Point out to pupils that the statement 'as heavy as' means that the two objects have the same mass.
- Ask pupils to look at the picture of the apple and orange. The apple is as heavy as the orange, which shows that the mass of the apple is the same as the mass of the orange.
- Demonstrate using a pan balance and different objects or modelling clay moulded into different shapes.

**4**

- Ask pupils to explain why the marble is heavier than the plastic ball or why the plastic ball is lighter than the marble.

---

Mass **Unit 10**

**3** apple    orange

The apple is **as heavy as** the orange.

**4**

 marble    ball

Which is heavier?

Which is lighter?

The marble is heavier.

The ball is lighter.

7

## What you will need

- A pan balance
- Small bag of flour and small bag of sugar with the same mass
- Small bag of rice with larger mass

## Teaching sequence

- Look for pupils who can identify the heaviest or lightest object by looking at the pan balance. Encourage pupils to use the terms 'heaviest' and 'lightest'.
- Demonstrate using the bags of flour, sugar and rice.
- Look for pupils who notice that the bag of sugar is as heavy as the bag of flour. Then they should be able to infer that the bag of rice is heavier than the bag of sugar.

- Look for pupils who can explain which of the three objects is the heaviest or lightest.

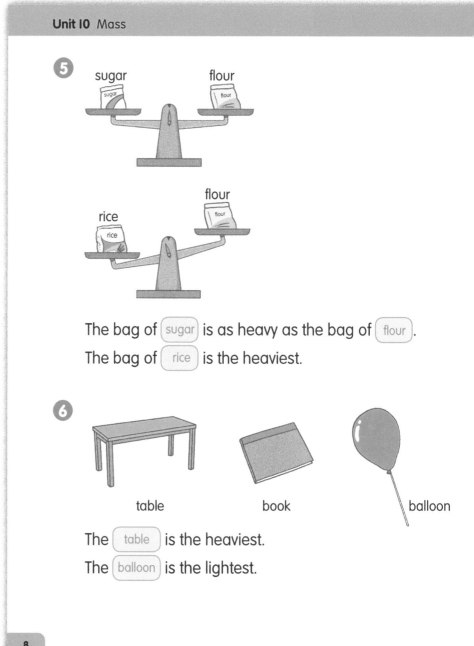

## What you will need

- A pan balance
- A leaf, a ruler, a rubber, a pencil, a sharpener and a crayon for each group

**Activity**

**7** Guess which is heavier in each set.

Use a pan balance to check your answers.

a
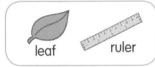
leaf    ruler

b
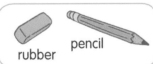
rubber    pencil

c

sharpener    crayon

| My guess | It is |
|---|---|
| a | a |
| b | b |
| c | c |

9

## Teaching sequence

**7**

- Ask pupils to work in groups.
- Ask pupils to guess the heavier or lighter object in each set as shown in the textbook and record their guesses in a table.
- Then ask pupils to use the pan balance to compare the objects to find out which is heavier or lighter and record their findings in the same table.
- Encourage pupils to share their results with the class.

## Note

Use the activity below to introduce the concept of measurement by weighing two different objects.

## What you will need

- A pan balance
- Ruler
- Empty plastic bottle
- Modelling clay
- 3 different objects from around the classroom

## Independent work

Practice I in Practice Book IC, pp 5 to 10.

Provide a pan balance and the items listed on Page 9 of the Practice Book for pupils to check their answers.

## Teaching sequence

- Ask pupils to follow the steps shown to carry out the activity.
- Encourage pupils to discuss their answers.
- Use the example below to further reinforce the concept:
  (a) Select 3 different objects from around the classroom. Arrange the items from the heaviest to the lightest and label them A, B and C.
  (b) Ask pupils to measure the 3 objects in turn.
  (c) Point out that A is heavier than B and B is heavier than C. Therefore A is the heaviest item of the three and C is the lightest.

## Activity

8  You will need a pan balance, a ruler, an empty plastic bottle and some modelling clay.

I   Put the ruler on one side of the pan balance.

Use the modelling clay to make a ball as heavy as the ruler.

Name it Ball A.

2   Put the plastic bottle on one side of the pan balance.

Use the modelling clay to make another ball as heavy as the plastic bottle.

Name it Ball B.

3   Answer these questions.

a   Which ball is heavier, A or B?

b   Which is heavier, the ruler or the bottle?

Practice Book IC, p.5

10

## Learning objectives: Finding the masses of things

**Pupils will be able to:**

- use a non-standard object such as a marble to find the masses of objects
- compare objects using a non-standard object as a medium of measurement

## Key concept

Mass can be measured using objects as non-standard units.

## Thinking skills

- Comparing
- Deduction

## What you will need

- A pan balance
- A number of identical non-standard units, e.g., marbles, cubes, clothes pegs or paper clips
- Common objects, e.g., mugs, books

## Additional activity

Ask pupils to find the comparative masses of other objects found in the classroom.

## Objective of activity

Pupils will be able to find the number of identical non-standard units required to represent the mass of an object.

---

# Let's Learn!

### Finding the masses of things

**1**

 The mug is as heavy as 10 marbles.

The mass of the mug is 10 marbles.

**2**

**a** The mass of Bag A is [ 2 ] marbles.

**b** Bag B is as heavy as [ 3 ] marbles.

**c** Which is the lightest bag? [Bag A]

**d** Which is the heaviest bag? [Bag C]

**e** Bag [B/C/C] is heavier than Bag [A/B/A].

**f** Bag [A/A/B] is lighter than Bag [B/C/C].

11

---

## Teaching sequence

**1**

- Encourage pupils to recall the 'Finding length in units' section from Unit 9, Pupil Textbook 1A, where they used non-standard units such as drinking straws and paper clips to find the lengths of items. Point out that this is a similar method to the one being used to find the masses of objects.
- Point out the picture of the mug balanced with 10 marbles. Say: "*The mug is as heavy as 10 marbles.*" and "*The mass of the mug is 10 marbles.*"

**2**

- Ask pupils to find the masses of A, B and C in terms of the numbers of marbles and then compare the numbers of marbles to determine which is the heaviest or lightest object.

## Thinking skills
- Comparing
- Deduction

## Objectives of activity
Pupils will be able to:
- use a pan balance to compare the masses of three objects and state the heaviest or the lightest object
- arrange the masses of the objects in decreasing order

## Teaching sequence

 **3**

**a**
- Ask pupils to work in groups to find the masses of the objects shown using the marbles. Ask pupils to record their answers in a table and present the results.

**b**
- Ask pupils to work in small groups. Ask each group to select one item from their boxes, without letting other groups see what they have selected.
- Encourage pupils to determine the mass of their mystery object using the non-standard units and the pan balance. Then ask pupils to write the mass of their mystery object on an index card: "*Our mystery object has a mass of _____ marbles.*"
- Ask pupils to put their mystery object back in the box and attach the index card to the front. Arrange all the boxes and cards in front of the class. Ask each group to go to each box in turn to guess and use the pan balance to find out what the mystery object was.
- To make it more challenging, set a time limit for each group and vary the objects in each box.

**4** *Let's Explore!*
- Ask pupils to carry out the activity and explain how they ordered the objects.

## What you will need
- A pan balance
- A number of identical non-standard units, e.g., marbles, cubes, clothes pegs or paper clips
- An apple, a sock, a pencil case
- Index cards
- A box for each group filled with 6 common objects, e.g., a glue stick, soft toy, box of crayons, water bottle, notebook, pen
- 3 objects of different masses, e.g., a book, an orange and a ball

## Independent work
Practice 2 in Practice Book IC, pp 11 to 14.

---

**Unit 10** Mass

### Activity

**3** **a**  Use marbles and a pan balance to find the masses of these objects.

an apple        a sock        a pencil case

**b**  **Guess the mystery object.**

You will need a box of objects.
Pick one object.
Find its mass using marbles.
Write its mass on a card.

Show some friends the box of objects and the card.
Ask them to guess what your mystery object is.
They can use marbles and a pan balance to check their guesses.

My mystery object has a mass of 10 marbles.

Practice Book IC, p.11

### Let's Explore!

**4**  Work in pairs.
You will need a pan balance and three different objects.
Use the pan balance to arrange the objects in order.
Begin with the heaviest object.

12

## Learning objectives: Finding mass in units

**Pupils will be able to:**

- find the masses of objects using non-standard units
- use the term 'units' in writing the masses of objects
- explain why there is a difference in using different objects as measuring units

## Key concept

Mass can be described using the term 'units'.

## Thinking skills

- Comparing
- Deduction

## What you will need

- A pan balance
- A number of identical non-standard units, e.g., marbles, cubes, clothes pegs or paper clips
- An apple

---

**Let's Learn!**

### Finding mass in units

1  stands for 1 unit.

The mass of the apple is about 4 units.

2  stands for 1 unit.

The mass of the same apple is about [ 5 ] units.

Why is the number of units different?

Different items are used to stand for 1 unit.

13

---

## Teaching sequence

**1**

- Find the mass of the apple using the pan balance and state the mass in terms of the number of marbles.
- Explain that 1 marble stands for 1 unit. Say: "*The mass of the apple is 4 units.*"

**2**

- Use a different non-standard unit to assess pupils' understanding.
- Look for pupils who notice that the apple is as heavy as 5 cubes or that the mass of the apple is 5 cubes/5 units.
- Explain to pupils that different non-standard units have different masses. To find the mass of an object, they will need fewer of a heavier non-standard unit or more of a lighter non-standard unit. Ask pupils to guess what the mass of the apple would be if paper clips are used as the non-standard unit – would it be more or less?

## Thinking skills

- Comparing
- Induction

## What you will need

- A pan balance
- A number of 2 types of identical non-standard units, e.g., paper clips and marbles
- Set 1 – 4 light objects (a pencil, a ruler, a rubber, scissors)
- Set 2 – 3 heavier objects (a pencil case, a water bottle, a box of colour pencils)

## Teaching sequence

- Ask pupils to work in small groups.
- Ask pupils to guess the masses of the items in Set 1 using paper clips and use the pan balance to check their guesses.
- Ask pupils to record their findings in a table.

---

**Unit 10** Mass

**Activity**

**3** Set 1

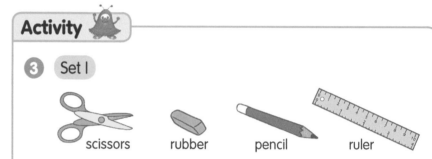

scissors    rubber    pencil    ruler

Use ✎ as 1 unit.

First guess the mass of each object.

Then check your answer with a pan balance.

| Object | Our guess | It is |
|---|---|---|
| Scissors | units | units |
| Rubber | units | units |
| Pencil | units | units |
| Ruler | units | units |

14

## What you will need

- A pan balance
- A number of identical non-standard units, e.g., marbles, cubes, clothes pegs or paper clips
- 5 objects found in the classroom, e.g., pencil case, small book, rubber

## Additional activity

Ask pupils to work in groups. Ask them to select 5 objects found in the classroom, then to find and record their masses using non-standard units.

Next ask pupils to arrange the objects in increasing or decreasing order of their masses.

Ask pupils to discuss their findings with the class.

## Activity

### Set 2

pencil case        water bottle        box of pencils

Use ⚪ as 1 unit.

First guess the mass of each object.

Then check your answer using a pan balance.

| Object | Our guess | It is |
|---|---|---|
| Pencil case | ☐ units | ☐ units |
| Water bottle | ☐ units | ☐ units |
| Box of pencils | ☐ units | ☐ units |

Next use ✐ as 1 unit to find the masses of the objects in Set 2. Are the answers the same?

Then use ⚪ to find the masses of the objects in Set 1. Are the answers the same? Can you say why?

15

## Teaching sequence

- Ask pupils to repeat these steps for the items in Set 2 using marbles. Ask them to record their results in a table.
- Then ask pupils to use paper clips to find the masses of the items in Set 2, and use marbles to find out the masses of the items in Set 1. Ask them to record their answers next to their original findings.
- Encourage pupils to explain their answers.
- **Note**: Pupils may find that they may not have sufficient paper clips to balance the items in Set 2, while the items in Set 1 may be too light for even 1 marble.
- For pupils who need additional support, explain that heavier non-standard units (e.g. marbles) are more suitable to be used for finding the masses of heavier objects (e.g. Set 2); while lighter non-standard units (e.g. paper clips) are more suitable for finding the masses of lighter objects (e.g. Set 1).

## Teaching sequence

- Encourage pupils to answer the questions. Assess their understanding of the use of non-standard units to measure and compare masses, as well as how to compare and arrange objects in order of their masses.

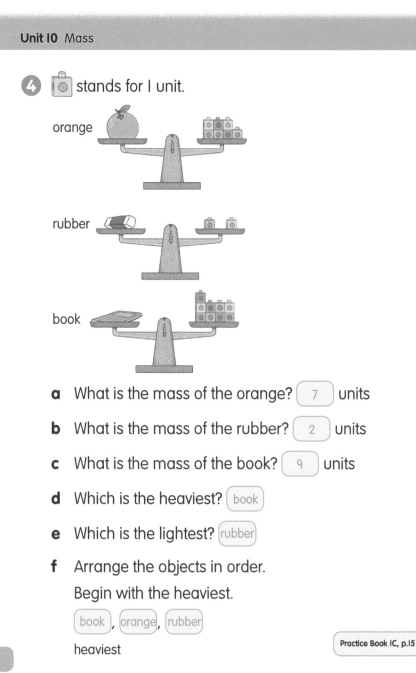

**Unit 10** Mass

4 🔲 stands for 1 unit.

orange

rubber

book

a   What is the mass of the orange?   7   units

b   What is the mass of the rubber?   2   units

c   What is the mass of the book?   9   units

d   Which is the heaviest?  book

e   Which is the lightest? rubber

f   Arrange the objects in order.
    Begin with the heaviest.

    book , orange , rubber

    heaviest

Practice Book IC, p.15

16

## Objective of activity

Pupils will be able to use comparing and deduction when given a set of measurements to arrange masses in order.

## Thinking skills

- Comparing
- Deduction
- Sequencing

## Heuristics for problem solving

- Act it out
- Guess and check
- Simplify the problem

## Independent work

*Challenging Practice, Problem Solving* and *Maths Journal* in Practice Book IC, pp 19 to 22.

# Put On Your Thinking Caps!

**5** **a**

Which bag is heavier, A or B? A

**b**

Arrange the boxes in order.
Begin with the lightest. A, B, C

Practice Book IC, p.19   Practice Book IC, p.21

17

## Teaching sequence

**5** *Put On Your Thinking Caps!*

**a**

- Ask pupils to look at the picture and describe what they notice about Bag A and Bag B.
- Ask them which bag is heavier, and to explain their answer. (Bag A is heavier, as Bag B needs to have additional weights to balance Bag A).
- If needed, use a pan balance to show what happens when the additional weights are removed.

**b**

- Ask pupils to arrange the boxes in order and to explain their answer.

**Unit 10:** Mass   15

# INSPIRE MATHS

# PRACTICE BOOK 1C

Consultant and author
Dr Fong Ho Kheong

**Authors**
Chelvi Ramakrishnan and Bernice Lau Pui Wah

**UK consultants**
Carole Skinner, Simon d'Angelo and Elizabeth Gibbs

---

## Unit 10  Mass

Date: _____

### Practice 1  Comparing things

1  Look at the fruits.
Write **heavy** or **light**.

banana
heavy

grape
light

2  Write **heavier** or **lighter**.

a

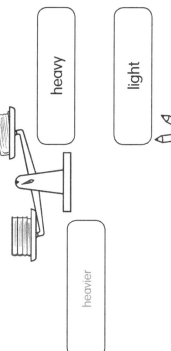

heavier

heavy

b

lighter

light

**4** Fill in the spaces.

**a**

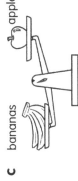

The _____ mug _____ is heavier than the _____ cup _____.

The _____ cup _____ is lighter than the _____ mug _____.

**b**

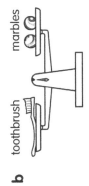

The _____ toy car _____ is heavier than the _____ cubes _____.

The _____ cubes _____ are lighter than the _____ toy car _____.

---

**3** Fill in the spaces with **heavier than**, **lighter than** or **as heavy as**.

**a**

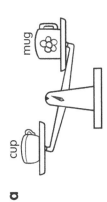

strawberry    bread

The bread is _____ heavier than _____ the strawberry.

The strawberry is _____ lighter than _____ the bread.

**b**

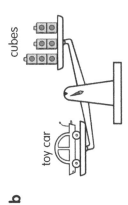

toothbrush    marbles

The toothbrush is _____ as heavy as _____ the marbles.

The marbles are _____ as heavy as _____ the toothbrush.

**c**

bananas    apple

The apple is _____ lighter than _____ the bananas.

The bananas are _____ heavier than _____ the apple.

**c**

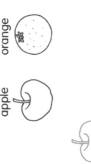

The ___rice___ is heavier than the ___sugar___ .

The ___sugar___ is lighter than the ___rice___ .

**d** Ella has an apple and an orange.
She puts them on a pan balance.
The orange is heavier than the apple.

Draw the apple and orange on the correct pans.

apple   orange

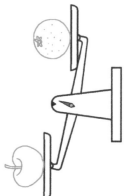

---

**5** Guess which object is heavier.
Tick (✓) your guess.
Then check using a pan balance.
Tick (✓) the heavier object.

| My guess | | It is | |
|---|---|---|---|
| orange | scissors | orange | scissors |
| book | a piece of paper | book | a piece of paper |
| a piece of paper | 2 paper clips | a piece of paper | 2 paper clips |
| orange | book | orange | book |

How many correct guesses did you make? ___Answers vary___

## Practice 2   Finding the masses of things

Fill in the spaces with the correct numbers.

1.

clothes pegs      ball

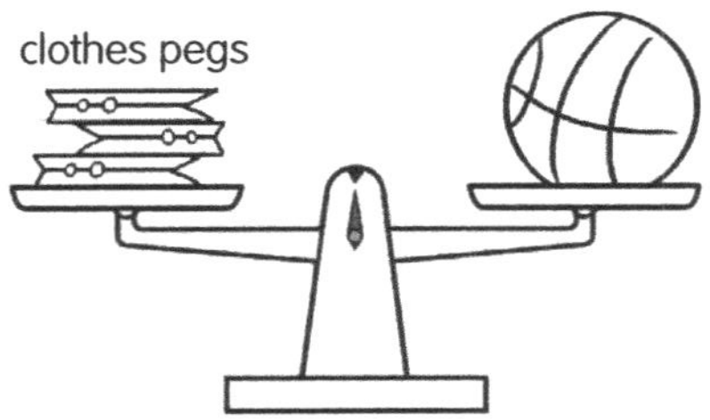

The mass of the ball is ___3___ clothes pegs.

2.

toy panda      toy bricks

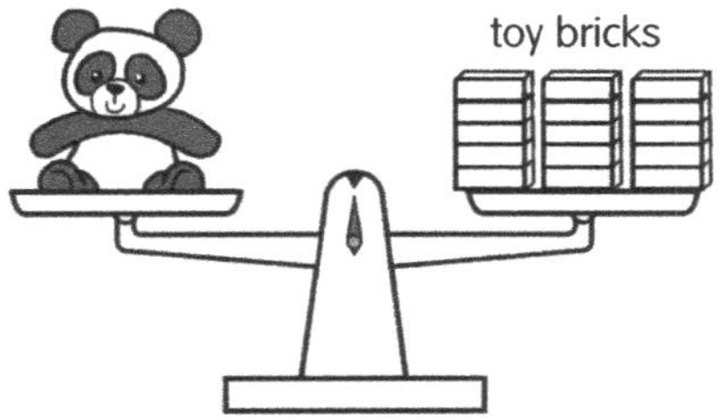

The mass of the toy panda is ___15___ toy bricks.

---

**6** Look at the things.
Fill in the spaces.

a

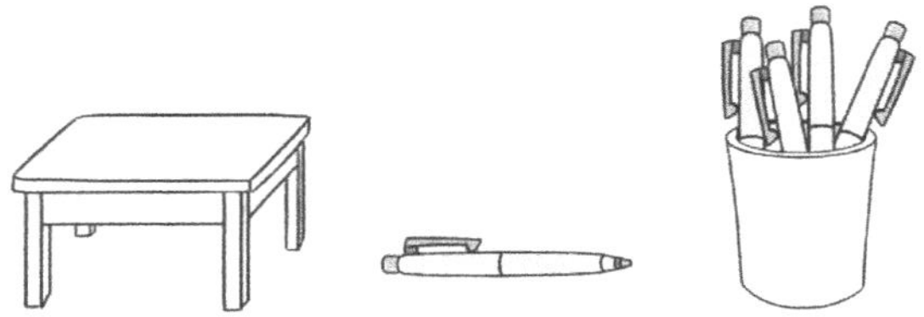

table      pen      pot of pens

The ___table___ is the heaviest.

The ___pen___ is the lightest.

b

stapler      coin      book

The ___book___ is the heaviest.

The ___coin___ is the lightest.

**3**

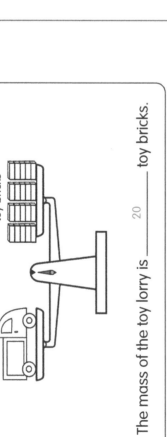

toy lorry  
toy bricks

The mass of the toy lorry is ___20___ toy bricks.

**4**

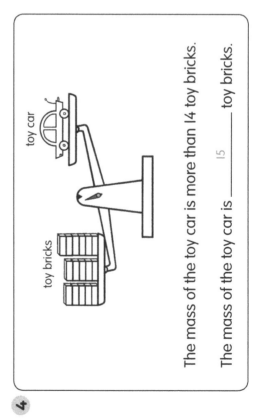

toy bricks  
toy car

The mass of the toy car is more than 14 toy bricks.

The mass of the toy car is ___15___ toy bricks.

**5** Look at the pictures.
Then fill in the spaces.

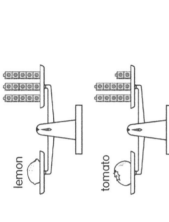

lemon

tomato

orange

**a** The mass of the lemon is ___15___ cubes.

**b** The mass of the tomato is ___12___ cubes.

**c** The mass of the orange is ___20___ cubes.

**d** The lemon is heavier than the ___tomato___.

**e** The lemon is lighter than the ___orange___.

**f** The ___orange___ is the heaviest.

**g** The ___tomato___ is the lightest.

**h** Arrange the fruit in order.

___orange___, ___lemon___, ___tomato___
heaviest

## Practice 3   Finding mass in units

1 Fill in the spaces.

a Use ⚾ as 1 unit.

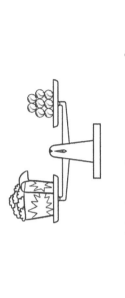

The mass of the box of popcorn is __8__ units.

b Use ▢ as 1 unit.

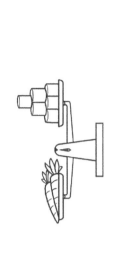

The mass of the carrots is __6__ units.

---

6 Look at the pictures.
Then fill in the spaces.

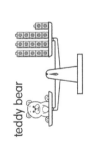

toy train

ball

teddy bear

a The mass of the toy train is __10__ cubes.

b The mass of the ball is __6__ cubes.

c The mass of the teddy bear is __17__ cubes.

d The __toy train / teddy bear__ is heavier than the ball.

e The __toy train / ball__ is lighter than the teddy bear.

f The toy train is heavier than the __ball__.

g The __Answers vary__ is lighter than the __Answers vary__.

h The heaviest toy is the __teddy bear__.

i The lightest toy is the __ball__.

j Arrange the toys in order.

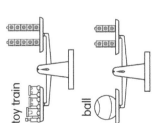

__ball__, __toy train__, __teddy bear__
lightest

c Use 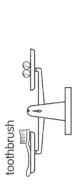 as 1 unit.

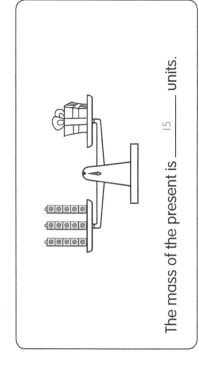

The mass of the present is ___15___ units.

d Use ⬭ as 1 unit.

The mass of the lemon is ___6___ units.

2 Fill in the spaces.
Use ⬭ as 1 unit.

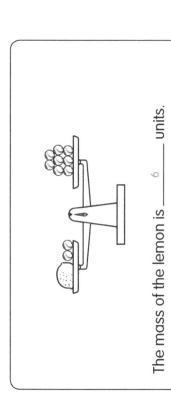

toothbrush    soap    shampoo

a The mass of the toothbrush is ___2___ units.

b The mass of the soap is ___5___ units.

c The mass of the shampoo is ___10___ units.

d The ___toothbrush___ is lighter than the soap.

e The shampoo is heavier than the ___toothbrush / soap___.

f The ___shampoo___ is the heaviest.

g The ___toothbrush___ is the lightest.

## 3 Fill in the spaces.
Use ◎ as 1 unit.

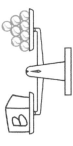 **A**
 **B**

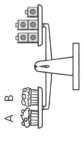 **C**
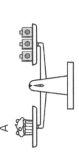 **D**

a The mass of Box A is __9__ units.

b The mass of Box B is __7__ units.

c The mass of Box C is __10__ units.

d The mass of Box D is __6__ units.

e Box __C__ is the heaviest.

f Box __D__ is the lightest.

g Box __A / B / C__ is heavier than Box D.

h Box __B / D__ is lighter than Box A.

i Put the boxes in order.

 C   A   B    D
heaviest

---

Date: _____

## Challenging Practice

**1** Read the sentences below.

Box A has a mass of 6 marbles.
Box B is 2 marbles heavier than Box A.

Draw the marbles for Box A and Box B.

 A
 B

**2** What is the mass of Cake B?

A
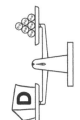
A  B

The mass of Cake B is __2__ 🍰.

**3** Write **mango** or **watermelon** in the spaces.

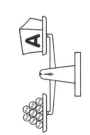 watermelon
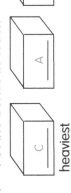 mango

The __mango__ is heavier than the __watermelon__.

## Problem Solving

**1** Look at the pictures.

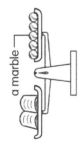
school bag    water bottle

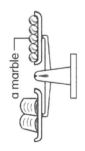
school bag    lunch box

water bottle    lunch box

Arrange the objects in order of their masses.

heaviest  school bag , lunch box , water bottle

---

**4** Look at the pictures.
Then answer the question.

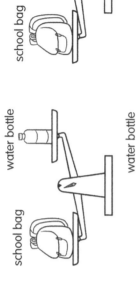
stapler        a block        a marble

Which is heavier, a block or a marble?  a block

**5** Fill in the spaces.

scissors    stapler
scissors    pen

a  The  stapler  is heavier than the scissors.

b  The  pen  is lighter than the scissors.

c  Arrange the things in order.

lightest  pen , scissors , stapler

**6**

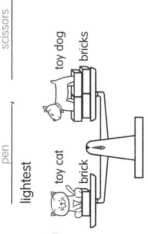
toy cat    toy dog
brick      bricks

Which is heavier, the toy cat or the toy dog?  toy cat

Why?  The toy cat plus one brick is as heavy as

the toy dog plus four bricks.

Date: _____

## Maths Journal

Look at the pictures below.

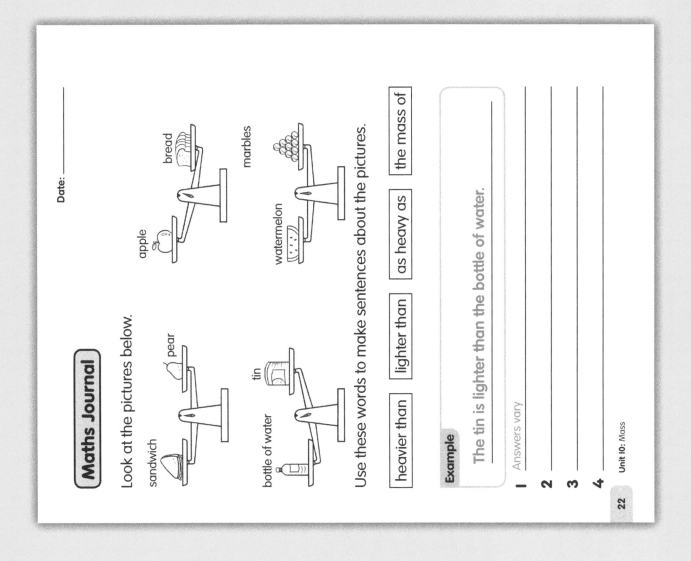

sandwich — pear

apple — bread

bottle of water — tin

watermelon — marbles

Use these words to make sentences about the pictures.

| heavier than | lighter than | as heavy as | the mass of |

**Example**

The tin is lighter than the bottle of water.

Answers vary

1 _____

2 _____

3 _____

4 _____

22    Unit 10: Mass

# Unit 11: Picture Graphs

| Week | Learning Objectives | Thinking Skills | Resources |
|---|---|---|---|
| 3 | **(1) Simple picture graphs**<br><br>Pupils will be able to:<br>• collect and sort data for presentation, e.g., stickers of different colours<br>• arrange and present data in a table as a picture graph<br>• explain reasons for drawing picture graphs<br>• read and interpret the data given in the table<br>• count and find the number of each category of items<br>• compare two or more sets of data in picture graphs using the terms 'more than', 'fewer than', 'most' and 'least' | • Comparing<br><br>Heuristic for problem solving:<br>• Make a table | • Pupil Textbook 1B, pp 18 to 20<br>• Practice Book 1C, pp 23 to 26<br>• Teacher's Guide 1B, pp 28 to 30 |
| 3 | **(2) More picture graphs**<br><br>Pupils will be able to practise carrying out the whole process of collecting data, organising, drawing picture graphs and interpreting data. | • Comparing | • Pupil Textbook 1B, pp 21 to 24<br>• Practice Book 1C, pp 27 to 32<br>• Teacher's Guide 1B, pp 31 to 34 |

# Unit 11: Picture Graphs

Medium-term plan

| Week | Learning Objectives | Thinking Skills | Resources |
|---|---|---|---|
| 3 | *Put On Your Thinking Caps!* <br><br> Pupils will be able to: <br> • use the information provided to draw a picture graph on the numbers of rainy days and sunny days in a week <br> • interpret the graph to work out whether there are more sunny days or rainy days and to count how many more | • Classifying <br> • Comparing <br><br> Heuristic for problem solving: <br> • Make a list | • Pupil Textbook 1B, p 25 <br> • Practice Book 1C, pp 33 to 35 <br> • Teacher's Guide 1B, p 35 |

## Summative assessment opportunity

Assessment Book I, Test 5, pp 59 to 67

# Picture Graphs

## Learning objectives: Simple picture graphs

**Pupils will be able to:**

- collect and sort data for presentation, e.g., stickers of different colours
- arrange and present data in a table as a picture graph
- explain reasons for drawing picture graphs
- read and interpret the data given in the table

## Teaching sequence

- You could use pictures of the coloured stickers or stickers for this activity.
- Ask pupils to count the number of stickers in total. Then ask them to count the number of stickers of each different colour.
- Explain to pupils that they can group them according to colour and then organise them in a pictorial graph form.

- count and find the number of each category of items
- compare two or more sets of data in picture graphs using the terms 'more than', 'fewer than', 'most' and 'least'

## Key concept

Data can be collected and organised into a horizontal or vertical picture graph for interpretation.

## Objective of activity

Pupils will be able to collect and organise data in a systematic manner.

## What you will need

- Stickers or pictures of stickers: 5 red, 7 blue and 4 yellow
- Adhesive tack

Let's Learn!

**Simple picture graphs**

*Collecting and organising data*

 Sally loves stickers!
Count the number of stickers she has.

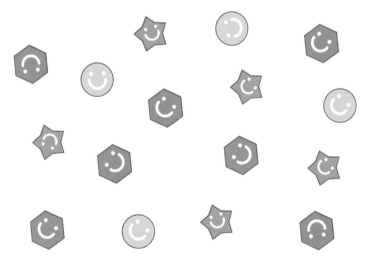

18

Additional activity
Encourage pupils to add
additional statements to
describe the graph.

Picture Graphs **Unit II**

We can show the number of stickers in this way too.

**Sally's Stickers**

| Red | Blue | Yellow |

There are 5 red stickers.

There are 7 blue stickers.

There are 4 yellow stickers.

There are 2 more blue stickers than red stickers.

There are 3 fewer yellow stickers than blue stickers.

Altogether there are 16 stickers.

19

## Teaching sequence

- Ask pupils to look at the graph in the textbook. Point out that the stickers can be organised in a vertical picture graph.
- Explain that the same set of stickers can also be presented in a horizontal graph.
- Read through the statements below the graph together. Look for pupils who can use statements like these to describe the graph.

Comparing

Additional activity
Encourage pupils to add additional statements to describe the graph.

Independent work
Practice I in Practice Book IC, pp 23 to 26.

## Teaching sequence

- Look for pupils who can make statements about the data in the graph.
- Encourage pupils to count the number of each type of animal and compare 2 types of animals using the terms 'more' or 'fewer'.

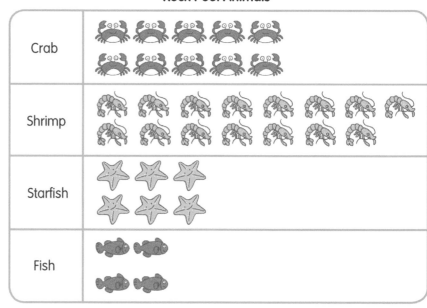

Unit II  Picture Graphs

### Interpreting data

2  These animals live in a rock pool.

**Rock Pool Animals**

| | |
|---|---|
| Crab | |
| Shrimp | |
| Starfish | |
| Fish | |

a  How many shrimps are there?  I5

b  How many starfish are there?  6

c  How many fish are there?  4

d  How many crabs are there?  I0

e  Are there more shrimps or fish?  shrimps
How many more?  II

f  Are there fewer starfish or crabs?  starfish
How many fewer?  4

20

Practice Book IC, p.23

## Learning objectives:
## More picture graphs

**Pupils will be able to:**

- practise carrying out the whole process of collecting data, organising, drawing picture graphs and interpreting data

## Key concept

Data can be collected and organised into a horizontal or vertical picture graph using symbols.

## Thinking skill

Comparing

## What you will need

Dice

---

# Let's Learn!

## More picture graphs

### Collecting and organising data

**I** Ella rolls a dice.

Each ⭐ stands for I roll.

**Ella's Rolls**

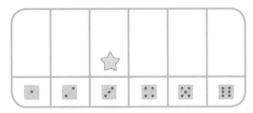

> Look at what I got!

Ella rolls the dice again.

**Ella's Rolls**

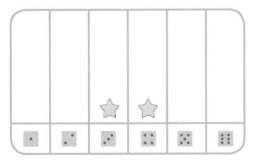

Help Ella roll the dice I0 more times.

Show the dice rolls on your own graph.

21

## Teaching sequence

**I**

- Ask pupils to work in groups.
- Guide them to carry out this activity and point out that this is the process of data collection. Ask them to record the outcome of every roll of the dice.
- Encourage pupils to complete a table of their results. Invite volunteers to present their results to the class.

## What you will need
- I red cube
- I blue cube
- I yellow cube
- I green cube
- A bag

## Additional activity
Ask pupils to look at the graph and write some statements. Then ask them to tell a story using these statements.

## Teaching sequence

- Ask pupils to work in small groups to follow the steps and carry out the activity.
- Ask them to record the result of each selection from the bag in the chart.
- Ask pupils to compare and discuss their results.

**Unit II** Picture Graphs

### Activity

2 Jack's bag contains I ▣, I ▣, I ▣ and I ▣.

Jack picks I ▣ from the bag.

He puts a **X** on the chart.

| ▣ | **X** |
|---|---|
| ▣ | |
| ▣ | |
| ▣ | |

Jack puts the ▣ back into the bag.

Help him pick another one.

Put a **X** on your own chart.

Do this 10 times.

Which ▣ did you pick the most times?

Which ▣ did you pick the fewest times?

Use **X** to show each pick.

Look out for opportunities to help your child collect data and make a chart or graph together. For example, you could make a chart of different coloured socks in a drawer. Ask your child questions about what you have found out.

22

Objective of activity
Pupils will be able to interpret data from graphs that are represented by symbols.

Additional activity
Ask pupils to say or write additional statements to explain the graph. They could work in pairs or groups.

Picture Graphs **Unit II**

## *Interpreting data*

**3** This graph shows the favourite toys of 20 children.

**Children's Favourite Toys**

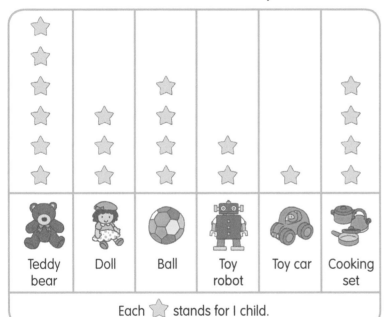

Each  stands for I child.

4 children like cooking sets.

3 children like dolls.

2 more children like balls than toy robots.

3 fewer children like toy cars than cooking sets.

The same number of children like balls and cooking sets.

There are 6 types of toys altogether.

The most popular toy is the teddy bear.

23

**Teaching sequence**

**3**

- Read through the statements together and point out the corresponding symbols on the graph.
- Ask questions about the graph to assess pupils' understanding. E.g., Ask: *"How many children like teddy bears?"*

  Then encourage pupils to say: *"6 children like teddy bears."*

Encourage pupils to say or write additional statements to explain the graph. They could work in pairs or groups.

Practice 2 and *Maths Journal* in Practice Book IC, pp 27 to 33.

## Teaching sequence

- Ask pupils to look at the picture graph and to explain what is shown by the graph. Look for pupils who can say that each blue circle stands for I child.
- Ask questions about the graph to assess pupils' understanding.
- Ask pupils to work in groups to write 3 more questions for the other groups to answer.

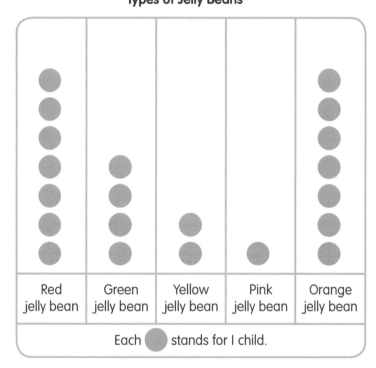

**Unit II** Picture Graphs

4 The graph shows the types of jelly beans that children like.

**Types of Jelly Beans**

Each ⬤ stands for I child.

How many children like orange jelly beans? 7

Which jelly beans do the fewest children like? pink jelly beans

How many more children like red jelly beans than green jelly beans? 3 more

How many fewer children like yellow jelly beans than orange jelly beans? 5 fewer

How many types of jelly beans are there? 5

24

Practice Book IC, p.27

## Objectives of activity

Pupils will be able to:
- use the information provided to draw a picture graph on the numbers of rainy days and sunny days in a week
- interpret the graph to work out whether there are more sunny days or rainy days and to count how many more

## Thinking skills
- Classifying
- Comparing

## Heuristic for problem solving

Make a list

## Independent work

*Challenging Practice* in Practice Book IC, pp 34 to 35.

# Put On Your Thinking Caps!

**5** Read the sentences.

Copy the graph. Fill it in.

It rains on Monday and Tuesday.

It is sunny on Wednesday and Thursday.

There is rain on Friday.

It is hot and does not rain on Saturday and Sunday.

Use ▲ to stand for I day.

**Sunny Days and Rainy Days**

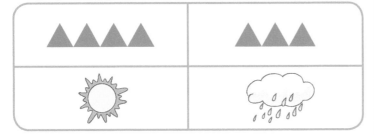

Are there more sunny days or rainy days? sunny days

How many more? I more

Practice Book IC, p.34

25

## Teaching sequence

**5** *Put On Your Thinking Caps!*

- Encourage pupils to read and follow the steps. For pupils who need additional support, ask them to write down the days of the week. Then read each statement together and record the weather for each day.

- Ask questions to help pupils organise their information into a picture graph.
  E.g.
  **Statement**: *"It rains on Monday and Tuesday."*

  **Question**: *"Is Monday a rainy day? If so, draw a triangle in the 'Rainy day' column."*

  **Question**: *"Is Tuesday a rainy day? If so, draw a triangle in the 'Rainy day' column."*

- Ask pupils to count the number of triangles in each column and then answer the questions.

# Unit 11 Picture Graphs

Date: ____________

## Practice 1 Simple picture graphs

1 Jack's friends have birthdays in these months.

| | | | |
|---|---|---|---|
| Peter in March | Miya in February | Millie in January | Farha in April |
| Emma in January | Hannah in March | Tai in March | Hardeep in February |
| Ethan in January | Omar in April | Ruby in March | Ella in March |

Help Jack to complete his graph below.

**Months My Friends Have Birthdays**

| | | | |
|---|---|---|---|
| Ethan<br>Emma<br>Millie | Hardeep<br>Miya | Ella<br>Ruby<br>Tai<br>Hannah<br>Peter | Omar<br>Farha |
| January | February | March | April |

Then answer the questions.

**a** How many friends have birthdays in January?

3

**b** Which month do most of his friends have birthdays?

March

Fill in the spaces for questions **2** to **4**.

**2** Miya's garden is full of flowers.

**Flowers in Miya's Garden**

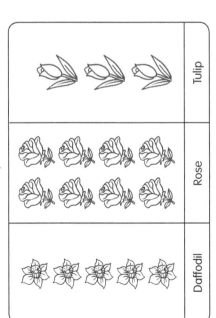

| Daffodil | Rose | Tulip |
|---|---|---|

**a** There are ___5___ daffodils.

**b** There are ___8___ roses.

**c** There are ___3___ tulips.

**d** There are ___5___ more roses than tulips.

**e** There are ___2___ fewer tulips than daffodils.

**f** There are ___16___ flowers altogether.

---

**3** Annie has a toy shop.

**Toys in Annie's Shop**

| Toy plane | | |
| Toy car | | |
| Toy train | | |

**a** There are ___3___ toy planes in Annie's shop.

**b** There are ___10___ toy cars.

**c** There are ___6___ toy trains.

**d** Annie has the most ___toy cars___ .

**e** Annie has the fewest ___toy planes___ .

**f** Annie has ___19___ toys altogether.

**g** There are ___4___ more toy cars than toy trains.

**h** There are ___7___ fewer toy planes than toy cars.

Date: _____

## Practice 2　More picture graphs

1　Peter has a counter.
Every time he tosses the counter, he gets ⭐ or ◁ .

Peter tosses the counter many times.
This is what he gets:

Count the tosses.
Colour a square for each toss.

**Peter's Tosses**

| ⭐ | | | | | | | | | |
|---|---|---|---|---|---|---|---|---|---|
| ◁ | | | | | | | | | |

Each ☐ stands for 1 toss.

a　⭐ comes up ___7___ times.

b　◁ comes up ___9___ times.

c　Colour the side that comes up more times.

d　Colour the side that comes up fewer times.

e　◁ comes up ___2___ more times than ⭐ .

---

4　The graph shows the coins Hardeep saves in a week.

**Hardeep's Savings**

| Monday | 10p | 10p | 10p | | | |
|---|---|---|---|---|---|---|
| Tuesday | 10p | 10p | 10p | 10p | | |
| Wednesday | | | | | | |
| Thursday | 10p | 10p | 10p | 10p | 10p | |
| Friday | 10p | | | | | |
| Saturday | 10p | 10p | 10p | | | |
| Sunday | 10p | 10p | 10p | 10p | | |

a　How many coins does Hardeep save on Monday?
He saves ___2___ coins.

b　How many coins does he save on Tuesday?
He saves ___4___ coins.

c　Hardeep saves 1 coin on Friday.
He saves ___2___ more coins on Saturday.

d　How many coins does he save from Thursday to
Saturday altogether? ___9___ coins

e　He does not save on ___Wednesday___ .

**2** The pictures below show the numbers Millie gets when she rolls a dice lots of times.

How many times does she get each number?
Colour the squares to show the number of times.

**Millie's Rolls**

| | | | | | | | | | |
|---|---|---|---|---|---|---|---|---|---|
| ⚁ | | | | | | | | | |
| ⚅ | | | | | | | | | |
| ⚃ | | | | | | | | | |
| ⚄ | | | | | | | | | |

Each ☐ stands for 1 time.

Fill in the spaces by drawing ⚁, ⚅, ⚃ or ⚄.

**a** Millie gets _____ the most times.

**b** She gets _____ the fewest times.

**c** She gets _____ and _____ the same number of times.

**3** Every child in Class IB has a pet.
The picture shows their pets.

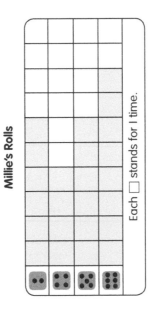

Count the pets and complete the graph.

**Class IB's Pets**

| Hamster | Goldfish | Mouse | Cat | Rabbit | Bird |
|---|---|---|---|---|---|
| △ | △ | △ | △ | | |
| △ | △ | △ | △ | △ | △ |
| | △ | △ | △ | | △ |
| | △ | △ | △ | | |
| | △ | | △ | | |
| 🐹 | 🐠 | 🐭 | 🐱 | 🐰 | 🐦 |

Each △ stands for I pet.

Fill in the spaces.

**a** The most popular pet is the _____. goldfish

**b** There are ___2___ more cats than birds.

**c** The least popular pet is the _____. rabbit

**d** There are equal numbers of _____ birds and _____ or cats and mice _____. hamsters

**Answers Unit II:** Picture Graphs

---

**4** Ruby goes to the wildlife park.
She makes a graph about the animals she sees.

**Animals in the Wildlife Park**

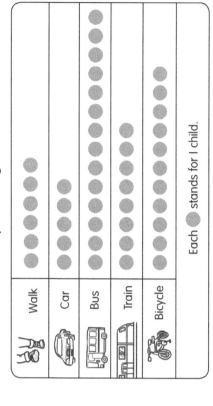

Tiger   Lion   Elephant   Giraffe   Rhinoceros

Each ⭐ stands for 1 animal.

Fill in the spaces.

a Ruby sees ___3___ tigers.

b She also sees ___6___ giraffes.

c She sees the most ___giraffes___.

d She sees the fewest ___lions___.

e There are ___2___ more rhinoceroses than lions.

f There are ___2___ fewer tigers than elephants.

---

**5** The graph below shows how the children in a class get to school.

**Ways of Getting to School**

Walk

Car

Bus

Train

Bicycle

Each ● stands for 1 child.

a How many children go to school by bus? ___14___

b ___8___ children go to school by train.

c How do most of the children go to school? ___bus___

d The fewest children go to school by ___car___.

e More children cycle than walk to school. How many more? ___5___

f Fewer children go to school by car than by bus. How many fewer? ___9___

## Maths Journal

1 Keep a record of how many books you read this week. Include the books you read in class and the books that are read to you.

Draw 📖 to represent I book.

Answers vary

**Number of Books I Read This Week**

| Monday | Tuesday | Wednesday | Thursday | Friday |
|--------|---------|-----------|----------|--------|
|        |         |           |          |        |

Each 📖 stands for I book.

Look at the graph you have completed. It tells you the number of books you have read. Write sentences about the number of books you have read. You can use the words below.

| more than | less than | most number | least number |

Answers vary

_____

_____

---

6 Some children drink different fruit juices at a party.

**Fruit Juices**

| Orange | Apple | Grape | Pineapple | Mixed fruit |
|--------|-------|-------|-----------|-------------|

Each 🥤 stands for I glass of juice.

a The children drink ___2___ glasses of grape juice.

b What is the most popular juice? ___Mixed fruit___

c They drink fewer glasses of apple juice than orange juice.

   How many fewer? ___4___

d How many types of juice do they drink? ___5___

e They drink ___20___ glasses of juice altogether.

Date: _____

## Challenging Practice

1  Look at the picture.

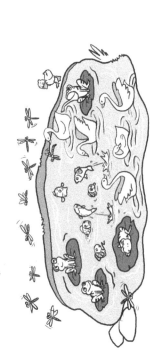

Use ☐ to stand for 1 animal.
Fill in the graph.

**Animals In and Around the Pond**

| Fish | ☐ ☐ ☐ ☐ |
| Swan | ☐ ☐ ☐ ☐ |
| Frog | ☐ ☐ |
| Dragonfly | ☐ ☐ ☐ ☐ ☐ ☐ ☐ ☐ |
| Duck | ☐ |

Each ☐ stands for 1 animal.

---

2  Team A, Team B and Team C play in a football competition. The graph shows the number of goals each child in Team A scores.

**Number of Goals for Team A**

| Ella | Omar | Miya | Jack |
|------|------|------|------|
| ● ● ● ● | ● ● ● ● ● ● | ● ● ● ● | ● ● ● |

Each ● stands for 1 goal.

a  How many goals does Team A score altogether?   17

b  Team B scores 7 fewer goals than Team A.
   How many goals does Team B score?   10

c  Team A scores 3 fewer goals than Team C.
   How many goals does Team C score?   20

# Medium-term plan

| Week | Learning Objectives | Thinking Skills | Resources |
|---|---|---|---|
| 4 | **(1) Counting to 40**<br><br>Pupils will be able to:<br>• recognise, read and write numbers from 21 to 40 and the corresponding numbers in words and concrete representation<br>• count within 40 by making tens first<br>• recognise and interpret sentences associated with tens and ones | • Analysing parts and whole | • Pupil Textbook 1B, pp 26 to 28<br>• Practice Book 1C, pp 37 to 40<br>• Teacher's Guide 1B, pp 48 to 50 |
| 4 | **(2) Place value**<br><br>Pupils will be able to:<br>• represent numbers as tens and ones in a place value chart<br>• show concrete representations in tens and ones given a number to 40<br>• write numerals given a set of concrete representations with or without place value charts | • Analysing parts and whole | • Pupil Textbook 1B, pp 29 to 30<br>• Practice Book 1C, pp 41 to 44<br>• Teacher's Guide 1B, pp 51 to 52 |

| Week | Learning Objectives | Thinking Skills | Resources |
|---|---|---|---|
| 4 | **(3) Comparing, order and pattern**<br><br>Pupils will be able to:<br>• use a strategy to compare numbers to 40<br>• compare numbers to 40 using the terms 'greater than' and 'smaller than' with or without concrete representation<br>• compare numbers to 40 using the terms 'greatest' and 'smallest' with or without concrete representation<br>• compare numbers to 40 using the terms 'more than' and 'less than' with or without concrete representation<br>• arrange numbers in ascending or descending order<br><br>*Maths Journal*<br><br>Pupils will be able to recall and apply the strategy for comparing numbers. | • Sequencing<br>• Comparing | • Pupil Textbook 1B, pp 31 to 36<br>• Practice Book 1C, pp 45 to 50<br>• Teacher's Guide 1B, pp 53 to 58 |

# Unit 12: Numbers to 40

| Week | Learning Objectives | Thinking Skills | Resources |
|---|---|---|---|
| 5 | **(4) Simple addition**<br><br>Pupils will be able to:<br>• add a 2-digit number and a 1-digit number without regrouping<br>• add a 2-digit number and another 2-digit number without regrouping<br>• use the 'counting on' strategy to add<br>• use the number bond strategy to add | • Analysing parts and whole | • Pupil Textbook 1B, pp 37 to 41<br>• Practice Book 1C, pp 51 to 54<br>• Teacher's Guide 1B, pp 59 to 63 |
| 5 | **(5) More addition**<br><br>Pupils will be able to:<br>• add a 2-digit number and a 1-digit number with regrouping<br>• add a 2-digit number and another 2-digit number with regrouping<br>• use the number bond strategy to add<br>• use the 'making ten' strategy to add | • Analysing parts and whole | • Pupil Textbook 1B, pp 42 to 46<br>• Practice Book 1C, pp 55 to 58<br>• Teacher's Guide 1B, pp 64 to 68 |

# Unit 12: Numbers to 40

| Week | Learning Objectives | Thinking Skills | Resources |
|---|---|---|---|
| 5 | **(6) Simple subtraction**<br><br>Pupils will be able to:<br>• subtract a 1-digit number from a 2-digit number without regrouping<br>• subtract a 2-digit number from another 2-digit number without regrouping<br>• use the 'counting back' strategy to subtract<br>• use the 'taking away' strategy to subtract<br>• use the number bond strategy to subtract | • Analysing parts and whole | • Pupil Textbook 1B, pp 47 to 51<br>• Practice Book 1C, pp 59 to 62<br>• Teacher's Guide 1B, pp 69 to 73 |
| 6 | **(7) More subtraction**<br><br>Pupils will be able to:<br>• subtract a 1-digit number from a 2-digit number with regrouping<br>• subtract a 2-digit number from another 2-digit number with regrouping<br>• apply the regrouping concept in subtraction<br>• use the number bond strategy to subtract | • Analysing parts and whole<br>• Comparing (numbers) | • Pupil Textbook 1B, pp 52 to 56<br>• Practice Book 1C, pp 63 to 66<br>• Teacher's Guide 1B, pp 74 to 78 |

| Week | Learning Objectives | Thinking Skills | Resources |
|------|---------------------|-----------------|-----------|
| 6 | **(8) Adding three numbers**<br><br>Pupils will be able to:<br>• add three 1-digit numbers to 40<br>• use the number bond strategy to add<br>• apply the 'making ten' strategy to add | • Analysing parts and whole<br>• Comparing (numbers) | • Pupil Textbook 1B, pp 57 to 58<br>• Practice Book 1C, pp 67 to 70<br>• Teacher's Guide 1B, pp 79 to 80 |
| 6–7 | **(9) Solving word problems**<br><br>Pupils will be able to:<br>• solve 1-step word problems in addition or subtraction<br>• apply the following concepts in addition: 'part-whole', 'adding on' and 'comparing'<br>• apply the following concepts in subtraction: 'part-whole', 'taking away' and 'comparing' | • Analysing parts and whole<br>• Comparing (numbers) | • Pupil Textbook 1B, pp 59 to 62<br>• Practice Book 1C, pp 71 to 72<br>• Teacher's Guide 1B, pp 81 to 84 |
| 7 | *Put On Your Thinking Caps!*<br><br>Pupils will be able to apply and use number bonds to 40 to make number sentences. | • Analysing parts and whole | • Pupil Textbook 1B, p 62<br>• Practice Book 1C, pp 73 to 74<br>• Teacher's Guide 1B, p 84 |
| | Review 4 | | • Practice Book 1C, pp 75 to 80 |

# Numbers to 40

## Learning objectives: Counting to 40

**Pupils will be able to:**

- recognise, read and write numbers from 21 to 40 and the corresponding numbers in words and concrete representation
- count within 40 by making tens first

- recognise and interpret sentences associated with tens and ones

## Key concepts
- Using one-to-one correspondence in counting
- 1 ten equals ten ones

## What you will need
40 cubes

## Teaching sequence

- Take 21 cubes and revise the counting on method to count from 1 to 21.
- Encourage pupils to count out loud:
  "1, 2, 3, 4, ... 21"

- Model the grouping process to regroup 21 to 2 tens and 1 one.
- Then show another method of counting: counting by tens and ones. Lead pupils to count on as follows:
  "10, 20 and 21"
  Or:
  "Ten, twenty, twenty-one."

Thinking skill
Analysing parts and whole

What you will need
40 cubes

Additional activity
Ask pupils to work in pairs. Pupils count numbers from 20 to 40 by taking turns to say the next number in the counting sequence.

Numbers to 40 **Unit I2**

**3**

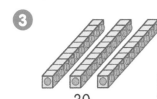

30

Ten, ... twenty, ... thirty, thirty-one, thirty-two, thirty-three, thirty-four, thirty-five

31, 32, 33, 34, 35

There are 35 .

**4** Count in tens and ones.
What are the numbers and words?

| Cubes | | Numbers | Words |
|---|---|---|---|
|  | | 24 | twenty-four |
| | | 27 | twenty-seven |
| | | 29 | twenty-nine |
| | | 36 | thirty-six |
| | | 38 | thirty-eight |

**5**
40
forty

I have 40 .

27

**Teaching sequence**

**3**

• Model the grouping process with this example and count on in tens and ones.
• Invite volunteers to count the number of cubes out loud.

**4**

• Look for pupils who can count numbers up to 40.
• Ask them to write in numerals and in words. Check that they are counting in tens and ones, instead of counting in ones.

**5**

• Introduce the number 40 in numerals and words.
• Use the cubes to relate the words, numerals and the concrete representation.

Ask pupils to work in pairs.

Pupil A calls out a number between 20 to 40. Pupil B then uses this number to make the statement:

"___ and ___ make ___."

Pupils A and B then swap roles.

**Independent work**

Practice I in Practice Book IC, pp 37 to 40.

## Teaching sequence

**6** and **7**

- Introduce various ways to show numbers from 20 to 40 using concrete representation. E.g. 28 can be expressed in two different ways:
  (a) 20 and 8 make 28
      $20 + 8 = 28$
  (b) 8 and 20 make 28
      $8 + 20 = 28$

**8**

- Ask pupils to work on the questions. Look for pupils who can add the tens and ones.

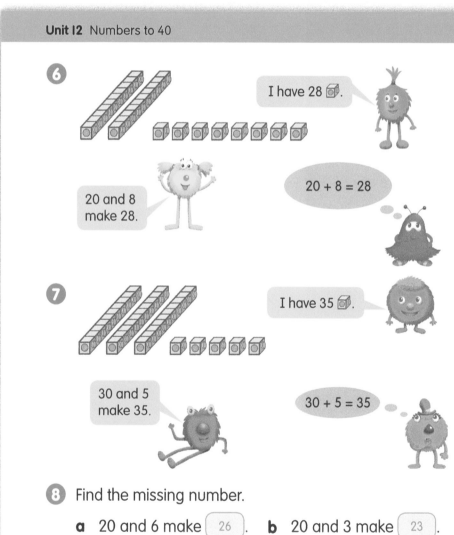

Unit I2  Numbers to 40

**6**

I have 28 🎲.

20 and 8 make 28.

$20 + 8 = 28$

**7**

I have 35 🎲.

30 and 5 make 35.

$30 + 5 = 35$

**8**  Find the missing number.

**a**  20 and 6 make 26 .  **b**  20 and 3 make 23 .

**c**  $20 + 8 =$ 28  **d**  7 and 30 make 37 .

**e**  9 and 30 make 39 .  **f**  $4 + 30 =$ 34

Practice Book IC, p.37

28

## Learning objectives: Place value

**Pupils will be able to:**

- represent numbers as tens and ones in a place value chart
- show concrete representations in tens and ones given a number to 40
- write numerals given a set of concrete representations with or without place value charts

## Key concept

Numbers to 40 can be represented as tens and ones in a place value chart.

## Thinking skill

Analysing parts and whole

## What you will need

- 40 small objects to use as counters, e.g., straws or cubes
- 3 containers or rubber bands
- base ten equipment

# Let's Learn!

**Place value**

| Tens | Ones |
|------|------|
| 2 | 3 |

20        3

23 = 2 tens 3 ones

23 = 20 + 3

 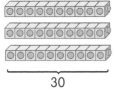 

30        6

| Tens | Ones |
|------|------|
| 3 | 6 |

36 = 3 tens 6 ones

36 = 30 + 6

29

## Teaching sequence

**1**

- Count and arrange 23 straws in a row. Make 2 sets of 10 straws using the containers or rubber bands and set these apart from the remaining counters.
- Introduce pupils to the concept of 2 tens and 3 ones with the help of a place value chart. Link it to the earlier concepts:
  - 20 and 3 make 23
  - 23 is 20 and 3
  - 23 is 2 tens 3 ones
- Show the numeral expression: $23 = 20 + 3$

**2**

- Show place values with alternative concrete representations using cubes and rods.
- Count and arrange 36 cubes. Make 3 sets of 10 cubes and set these apart from the remaining cubes.
- Similarly show different ways of representing place values:
  - $36 = 3$ tens $6$ ones
  - $36 = 30 + 6$

What you will need
- 40 straws
- 3 containers or rubber bands
- base ten equipment

Independent work

Practice 2 in Practice Book IC, pp 41 to 44.

## Teaching sequence

- Ask pupils to fill in the place value charts and sentences given the concrete representations of 28 and 37. Use this question to assess pupils' understanding.

- Ask pupils to work in groups to complete this activity.
- Give each group a set of numbers and ask them to present the numbers using concrete representation such as straws or cubes.

---

**Unit 12** Numbers to 40

3 **Find the missing numbers.**

a

| Tens | Ones |
|------|------|
| 2 | 8 |

28 = [ 2 ] tens [ 8 ] ones

b

| Tens | Ones |
|------|------|
| 3 | 7 |

37 = [ 3 ] tens [ 7 ] ones

**Activity**

4 You will need 40 straws.

Put them in tens and ones to show these numbers.

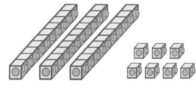

22    27    30    33    34    35

Practice Book IC, p.41

30

## Learning objectives: Comparing, order and pattern

**Pupils will be able to:**

- use a strategy to compare numbers to 40
- compare numbers to 40 using the terms 'greater than' and 'smaller than' with or without concrete representation
- compare numbers to 40 using the terms 'greatest' and 'smallest' with or without concrete representation
- compare numbers to 40 using the terms 'more than' and 'less than' with or without concrete representation
- arrange numbers in ascending or descending order

## Key concept

Numbers to 40 can be compared using the terms 'greater than'/'smaller than' and 'greatest'/'smallest' as well as arranged in ascending or descending order.

## Thinking skills

- Sequencing
- Comparing

## What you will need

- Number track or number line
- A calendar

---

Numbers to 40 **Unit 12**

# Let's Learn!

### Comparing, order and pattern

**1** This is a number track.

2 more          2 less

| 26 | 27 | 28 | 29 | 30 | 31 | 32 | 33 | 34 | 35 | 36 | 37 | 38 | 39 | 40 |

Count on from 27.          Count back from 38.

29 is 2 more than 27.  |  36 is 2 less than 38.

29 is greater than 27.  |  36 is smaller than 38.

**2** This picture shows part of a calendar.

24  is 2 more than 22.  |  28  is 3 less than 31.

24  is greater than 22.  |  28  is smaller than 31.

31

## Teaching sequence

**1**

- Show a number track or number line with numbers from 26 to 40. Revise the concepts of 'more than', 'less than', 'how many more than', 'how many less than', 'greater than' and 'smaller than' using the number track.
- Work through the example in the textbook together using the 'counting on' and 'counting back' strategies.
- Point out to pupils that we are comparing two numbers. We can use either 'more than' or 'less than' in comparing numbers.

  E.g. To compare 27 and 29, we can say that 27 is 2 less than 29 or 29 is 2 more than 27.
- Ask pupils to use two similar statements when comparing 36 and 38.

**2**

- Ask pupils to read the statements and use the calendar to find the answer. Use this question to assess pupils' understanding.

**What you will need**
- Place value chart
- Base ten equipment

**Additional activity**

Ask pupils to work in pairs.

Pupil A calls out two numbers between 20 to 40. Pupil B writes down the two numbers in a column, with one number above the other. Pupil B says which number is greater and explains why.

Pupils A and B swap roles.

## Teaching sequence

- Show the numbers 28 and 31 on place value charts with concrete representations using base ten equipment. Explain the steps for comparing which number is greater or smaller.

  **Step 1**: Compare the tens.

  **Step 2**: Compare the ones.

  Relate the concrete representations to the numbers to show which is greater.
- Explain that in this example, the 2 tens from 28 is less than 3 tens from 31. So 31 is greater than 28. There is no need to go on to the second step.
- You can also place the two numbers in a chart like this and compare the columns:

| Tens | Ones |
|------|------|
| 2    | 8    |
| 3    | 1    |

- Show the numbers 34 and 37 on place value charts with concrete representations using base ten equipment.
- Explain that in this example, the 3 tens from 34 is the same as 3 tens of 37. We move on to the next step to compare the ones:

  4 ones from 34 is less than 7 ones from 37. So 34 is less than 37.
- Show the two numbers in column format and compare.

---

**Unit 12** Numbers to 40

**3** Compare 28 and 31.

The tens are different.

Compare the tens. 3 tens is greater than 2 tens.

28

| Tens | Ones |
|------|------|
| 2    | 8    |

31

| Tens | Ones |
|------|------|
| 3    | 1    |

31 is greater than 28.

**4** Compare 34 and 37.

The tens are equal. We compare the ones.

7 is greater than 4.

34

| Tens | Ones |
|------|------|
| 3    | 4    |

37

| Tens | Ones |
|------|------|
| 3    | 7    |

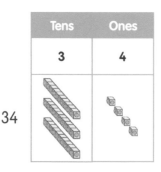

37 is greater than 34.

32

## Additional activity

Ask pupils to work in pairs.

Pupil A calls out a number between 20 and 40. Pupil B calls out another number that is slightly greater or smaller than the first number. Pupil A says whether the second number is greater or smaller, and explains why.

Pupils A and B swap roles.

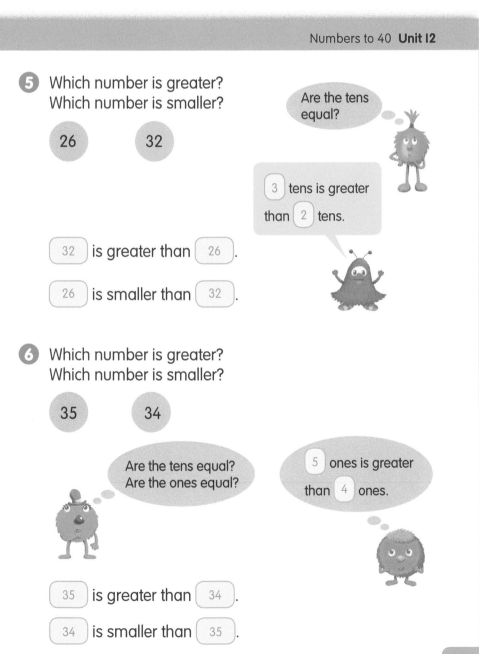

**5** Which number is greater?
Which number is smaller?

26      32

Are the tens equal?

3 tens is greater than 2 tens.

32 is greater than 26 .

26 is smaller than 32 .

**6** Which number is greater?
Which number is smaller?

35      34

Are the tens equal?
Are the ones equal?

5 ones is greater than 4 ones.

35 is greater than 34 .

34 is smaller than 35 .

33

## Teaching sequence

**5** and **6**

- Ask pupils to work on these examples.
- Encourage pupils to arrange the two numbers in columns before comparing.

| Tens | Ones |
|------|------|
| 2 | 6 |
| 3 | 2 |

Point out that the tens are different. 3 tens from 32 are greater than 2 tens from 26. So 26 is smaller than 32 or 32 is greater than 26.

| Tens | Ones |
|------|------|
| 3 | 5 |
| 3 | 4 |

Point out that the tens are the same. 5 ones from 35 are greater than 4 ones from 34. So 35 is greater than 34 or 34 is smaller than 35.

- Encourage pupils to use these statements to compare the numbers.

Additional activity

Ask pupils to work in pairs.

Pupil A calls out a number between 20 and 40. Pupil B calls out two other numbers, either greater or smaller than the original number, and writes down the three numbers on the board. Then Pupil A says which is the greatest number, which is the smallest number, and explains why.

Pupils A and B swap roles.

## Teaching sequence

- Show the numbers 27, 33 and 35 on place value charts and arrange 27 counters, 33 counters and 35 counters as shown.
- Work through the steps for comparing three numbers:

  **Step 1**: Compare the tens.
  ○ Explain that 27 is the smallest because 2 tens are smaller than 3 tens from 33 and 35.

  **Step 2**: Compare the ones.
  ○ Explain that 35 is greater than 33 because 5 ones are greater than 3 ones.
- Relate the concrete representation to the numbers to show which is the greatest.
- Alternatively, you can also arrange the three numbers in columns before comparing.

| Tens | Ones |
|------|------|
| 2    | 7    |
| 3    | 3    |
| 3    | 5    |

- Look for pupils who can use the steps modelled in 7.

---

**Unit 12** Numbers to 40

**7** Compare 27, 33 and 35.
Which is the greatest number?
Which is the smallest number?

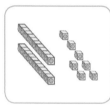  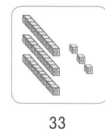  

27            33            35

The smallest number is [ 27 ].

Why is it the smallest number?

Why is 35 greater than 33?

The greatest number is [ 35 ].

**8** Find the greatest number.
Find the smallest number.

a ( 35 ) ( 34 ) ( 38 )   Greatest number: 38;
Smallest number: 34

b ( 27 ) ( 36 ) ( 30 )   Greatest number: 36;
Smallest number: 27

c ( 9 ) ( 18 ) ( 40 )   Greatest number: 40;
Smallest number: 9

34

**Additional activity**

Ask pupils to work in pairs.

Ask each pupil to draw a number track with some numbers missing. Then ask them to swap the number tracks with their partners and fill in the correct missing numbers to make a number pattern.

Invite volunteers to share their completed number tracks with the class.

**Independent work**

Practice 3 in Practice Book IC, pp 45 to 50.

**Teaching sequence**

**9**

- Show the number track with 3 missing numbers. Explain to pupils that the numbers on the track are arranged in a pattern and that they have to find the missing numbers.

- Explain and work through the steps below to help them find the missing numbers:

  **Step 1**: Check any two given adjacent numbers and use the 'more than or less than' concept to find the difference between them.

  **Step 2**: Check with other sets of given adjacent numbers to make sure that the difference between them is the same number.

  **Step 3**: Use this 'difference' to find the unknown numbers.

- Explain the strategy using the following:
  - 23 is 2 more than 21.
    37 is 2 more than 35.
    So the difference is 2.
  - 2 more than 25 is 27.
    The first unknown number is 27.
    2 less than 33 is 31.
    The second unknown number is 31.
    2 more than 37 is 39.
    The third unknown number is 39.

**10**

- Look for pupils who can apply this strategy to complete the pattern.

**9** The numbers on this number track are arranged in a pattern.
Some numbers are missing.

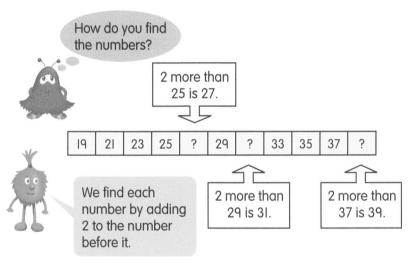

How do you find the numbers?

2 more than 25 is 27.

| 19 | 21 | 23 | 25 | ? | 29 | ? | 33 | 35 | 37 | ? |

We find each number by adding 2 to the number before it.

2 more than 29 is 31.

2 more than 37 is 39.

**10** The numbers below are arranged in a pattern.
Find the missing numbers.

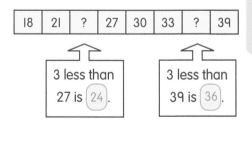

| 18 | 21 | ? | 27 | 30 | 33 | ? | 39 |

3 less than 27 is 24.

3 less than 39 is 36.

We find each number by subtracting 3 from the number after it.

Practice Book IC, p.45

35

## Objective of activity

Pupils will be able to recall and apply the strategy for comparing numbers.

## Teaching sequence

 *Maths Journal*

- This activity begins by helping pupils to revise the strategy and then requires pupils to use the strategy to solve the problems.

---

**Unit 12** Numbers to 40

## Maths Journal

**a** Omar completes this pattern.

32, 33, 34, 35, 36, 37, 38, 39

He writes these sentences to explain his thinking.

I add I to 32 to get 33.

I add I to 33 to get 34.

> 33 is I more than 32.
> 34 is I more than 33.

I just have to add I to get the next number.

I add I to 35.  →  35 + I = 36
I add I to 36.  →  36 + I = 37

How do you find the missing numbers in this pattern?

40, 30, ⬭20⬭, I0, ⬭0⬭

> Is the next number more or less?

**b** Use the words and numbers to help you fill in the spaces.

add I     add 5     add I0

subtract I     subtract 5     subtract I0

0     I     I0     20     30     40

I ⬭ to ⬭ to get ⬭.  add I0; I0; 20

I ⬭ from ⬭ to get ⬭.  subtract I0; 30; 20
subtract I0; I0; 0

36

---

## Learning objectives: Simple addition

**Pupils will be able to:**

- add a 2-digit number and a 1-digit number without regrouping
- add a 2-digit number and another 2-digit number without regrouping
- use the 'counting on' strategy to add
- use the number bond strategy to add

## Key concept

'Add on' and 'part-whole' concepts are used in adding numbers.

## Thinking skill

Analysing parts and whole

## What you will need

Base ten equipment

---

Numbers to 40  **Unit 12**

# Let's Learn!

**Simple addition**

**1** 24 + 3 = ?

> There are different ways to get the answer.

**a** Count on from 24.

| 24 | 25 | 26 | 27 |

24, **25, 26, 27**

**b** Use a place value chart.

| Tens | Ones |
|------|------|
| 24 | |
| 3 | |

First add the ones.

```
  Tens   Ones
    2      4
  +        3
  _____
           7
```

4 ones + 3 ones = 7 ones

```
   24  + 3
        4 + 3 = 7
        20 + 7 = 27
  20    4
```

Then add the tens.

```
  Tens   Ones
    2      4
  +        3
  _____
    2      7
```

2 tens + 0 tens = 2 tens

24 + 3 = 27

37

---

## Teaching sequence

**1**

**a**

- Introduce and explain the 'counting on' strategy with the help of a number track or number line.
- Explain to pupils that this strategy is efficient when the 1-digit is small, like it is in this question.

**b**

- Introduce and explain the vertical addition strategy with the help of a place value chart. Notice that no regrouping is needed in this section.
- Demonstrate and explain the following strategy using vertical addition:

  **Step 1**: Add the ones. 4 ones from 24 and 3 ones make 7 ones. Write the result in the ones column.

  **Step 2**: Add the tens. 2 tens and 0 tens make 2. Write the result in the tens column.

- The final answer is 2 tens 7 ones which is 27.
- You can relate number bonds to this problem and add the corresponding tens and ones. E.g. 2 tens and 0 tens make 2 tens. 4 ones and 3 ones make 7 ones. So combining them the result is 2 tens 7 ones which is 27.

Ask pupils to work in pairs.

Pupil A calls out two numbers: one 2-digit number and one I-digit number. The ones digits should not be regrouped when they are added. Ask Pupil B to use any method to add the two numbers.

Pupils A and B swap roles.

## Teaching sequence

- Look for pupils who can apply the following 3 strategies to add a I-digit number to a 2-digit number without regrouping:
  - 'Counting on' method
  - Vertical addition with place value chart
  - Using number bonds
- Explain to pupils that they can use any of these strategies to solve the problem.

---

**Unit 12** Numbers to 40

② 36 + 2 = ?

  **a** Count on from 36.

  **b** Use a place value chart.

First add the ones. Then add the tens.

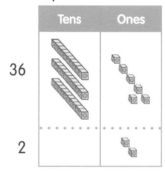

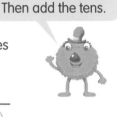

36 + 2 = [ 38 ]

38

**Teaching sequence**

③

**a**

- Introduce and explain the 'counting on' strategy with the help of a number track or number line if necessary. Explain to pupils the steps to add numbers:

  **Step 1**: Counting on in tens. E.g. 20, ....30

  **Step 2**: Counting on in ones. E.g. 30, 31, 32, ....37

- Ask pupils to talk about and practise the strategy.

**b**

- Introduce and explain the vertical addition strategy with the help of a place value chart. Notice that no regrouping is needed in this section. Show and explain the following strategy of adding the ones followed by adding the tens using vertical addition:

  **Step 1**: Add the ones. 0 one from 20 and 1 one from 17 make 7 ones. Write the result in the ones column.

  **Step 2**: Add the tens. 2 tens from 20 and 1 ten from 17 make 3 tens. Write the result in the tens column. The result is 3 tens 7 ones which is 37.

- Relate number bonds to this problem and add the corresponding tens and ones.

---

Numbers to 40  **Unit 12**

**③** 17 + 20 = ?

**a**  Count on from 20.

 20, ...**30**, ...**37**

**b**  Use a place value chart.

| Tens | Ones |
|------|------|
| 17 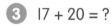 | |
| 20 | |

First add the ones.

| Tens | Ones |
|------|------|
| 1 | 7 |
| + 2 | 0 |
| | 7 |

7 ones + 0 ones = 7 ones

Then add the tens.

| Tens | Ones |
|------|------|
| 1 | 7 |
| + 2 | 0 |
| 3 | 7 |

1 ten + 2 tens = 3 tens

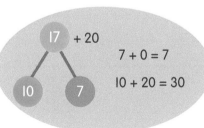

17 + 20

7 + 0 = 7

10 + 20 = 30

10   7

17 + 20 = 37

39

**Unit 12:** Numbers to 40   **61**

Ask pupils to work in pairs.

Pupil A calls out two numbers: one 2-digit number less than or equal to 40 and a tens number. Pupil B uses any method of their choice to add the two numbers.

Pupils A and B swap roles.

## Teaching sequence

- Look for pupils who can apply the 3 strategies to add tens to a 2-digit number without regrouping.
  - 'Counting on' method
  - Vertical addition with place value chart
  - Using number bonds
- Explain to pupils that they can use any of these strategies to solve the problem.

 and **6**

- Ask pupils to answer these questions to reinforce the strategies used above.

---

**Unit 12** Numbers to 40

**4** 20 + 10 = ?

   **a** Count on from 20.

20, ... 30

   **b** Use a place value chart.

| Tens | Ones |
|------|------|
| 20   |      |
| 10   |      |

First add the ones.
Then add the tens.

```
Tens  Ones
  2     0
+ 1     0
─────────
  3     0
```

2 tens + 1 ten = 3 tens

20 + 10 = 30

20 + 10 = 30

**5** 25 + 10 = 35

**6** 18 + 30 = 48

40

## Additional activity

Ask pupils to work in pairs.

Pupil A calls out two 2-digit numbers less than or equal to 40 where the sum of the ones digits is less than 10. Pupil B uses any method of their choice to add the two numbers.

Pupils A and B swap roles.

## Independent work

Practice 4 in Practice Book IC, pp 51 to 54.

 **7** 14 + 25 = ?

Use a place value chart.

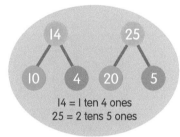 

14 = 1 ten 4 ones
25 = 2 tens 5 ones

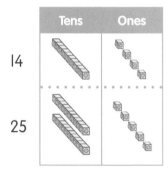

| Tens | Ones |
|------|------|
| 14 | |
| 25 | |

**First add the ones.**

```
   Tens   Ones
     1      4
 +   2      5
 _____
            9
```

4 ones + 5 ones = 9 ones

**Then add the tens.**

```
   Tens   Ones
     1      4
 +   2      5
 _____
     3      9
```

14 + 25 = 39

1 ten + 2 tens = 3 tens

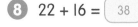 **8** 22 + 16 = [ 38 ]

Practice Book IC, p.51

41

## Teaching sequence

 **7**

- Introduce and explain the vertical addition strategy with the help of a place value chart. Notice that no regrouping is needed in this section. Demonstrate and explain the following strategy of adding the ones followed by adding the tens using vertical addition:

  **Step 1**: Add the ones.
  4 ones from 14 and 5 ones from 25 make 9 ones.
  Write the result in the ones column.

  **Step 2**: Add the tens.
  1 ten from 14 and 2 tens from 25 make 3 tens.
  Write the result in the tens column.
  The result is 3 tens 9 ones which is 39.

- You can relate number bonds to this problem and add the corresponding tens and ones.
  E.g. 14 = 1 ten and 4 ones
       25 = 2 tens and 5 ones
  1 ten and 2 tens make 3 tens.
  4 ones and 5 ones make 9 ones.
  So combining them the result is 3 tens and 9 ones which is 39.

**8**

- Look for pupils who can add two 2-digit numbers without regrouping using the vertical addition and number bond strategies.

## Learning objectives: More addition

**Pupils will be able to:**

- add a 2-digit number and a 1-digit number with regrouping
- add a 2-digit number and another 2-digit number with regrouping
- use the number bond strategy to add
- use the 'making ten' strategy to add

## Key concepts

- 'Add on' and 'part-whole' concepts are used in adding numbers
- Regrouping concept can be applied in addition

## Thinking skill

Analysing parts and whole

## What you will need

- 4 red counters and 20 green counters for each player
- Dice
- Place value chart for each player (see Photocopy master 1 on page 283)

## Teaching sequence

 *Game*

- Introduce this game to prepare pupils for the regrouping process using concrete representation. This helps pupils to link the concept to regrouping in addition in the following section.
- Model how to play the game. Explain regrouping before pupils begin the game. E.g. Pupils have to do 'trading' when they have 10 ones or more. If they have 12 ones then they have to regroup 12 ones to 1 ten and 2 ones and show these on their charts.

**2**

- Look for pupils who can carry out addition by regrouping.

---

**Unit 12** Numbers to 40

## Let's Learn!

### More addition

### Game

**1 Race to 40!**

How to play:

1 Red counters stand for tens. Green counters stand for ones.

3 Put this number of green counters on your chart. The other players take turns to roll the dice.

5 If you get 10 green counters, swap them for 1 red counter.

**Players:** 2 to 4
**You will need:**
- 4 red counters, 20 green counters and a place value chart for each player
- a dice

2 Roll the dice to get a number.

4 When it is your turn again, roll the dice. Add to the number of counters on your chart.

The first player to get 4 red counters or 4 tens wins!

**2** Regroup the ones into tens and ones. Use counters to help you.

| Tens | Ones | | Tens | Ones |
|------|------|---|------|------|
| 1 | 14 | = | 2 | 4 |

42

## Additional activity

Ask pupils to work in pairs.

Pupil A calls out two numbers: one 2-digit number less than or equal to 40 and one I-digit number. The sum of the ones digits should be greater or equal to 10. Pupil B uses any method of their choice to add the two numbers.

Pupils A and B swap roles.

Numbers to 40  **Unit 12**

**3** 28 + 6 = ?
Use a place value chart.

28 = 2 tens 8 ones

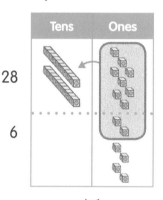

28

6

First add the ones.

|      | Tens | Ones |
|------|------|------|
|      |  2   |  8   |
|  +   |      |  6   |
|      |      |  4   |
|      |  I   |      |

8 ones + 6 ones = 14 ones

Regroup the ones.

14 ones = I ten 4 ones

Then add the tens.

|      | Tens | Ones |
|------|------|------|
|      |  2   |  8   |
|  +   |      |  6   |
|      |  3   |  4   |
|      |  I   |      |

2 tens + I ten = 3 tens

34

28 + 6 = 34

**Home Maths** Explain to your child that in the question above, 8 ones are added to 6 ones, which makes 14 ones altogether. 14 ones is the same as I ten and 4 ones. The tens need to be carried over to the tens column, so we write a small I in the tens column to show this.

43

## Teaching sequence

**3**

- Introduce and explain the vertical addition strategy with the help of a place value chart. Notice that regrouping is needed in this section. Show and explain the following strategy using vertical addition:

  **Step I**: Add the ones.
  8 ones from 28 and 6 ones make 14 ones.
  14 = I ten 4 ones after regrouping.
  Write 4 ones in the ones column, then write I ten in the tens column.

  **Step 2**: Add the tens.
  2 tens and I ten (regrouped from ones) make 3.
  Write the result in the tens column.
  The result is 3 tens and 4 ones, which is 34.

- Demonstrate regrouping using concrete representation.

## Additional activity

Ask pupils to repeat the 'Additional activity' from the previous page, and write the numbers in vertical addition format.

## Teaching sequence

**4**

- Look for pupils who can add a I-digit number to a 2-digit number by regrouping using vertical addition with a place value chart.
- Encourage pupils who need additional support to use concrete materials such as cubes.

**4** Add the numbers.

**a**

| Tens | Ones |
|------|------|
| 1 | 2 |
| + | 8 |
| 2 | 0 |

First add the ones.

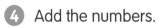

[ 2 ] ones + [ 8 ] ones = [ 10 ] ones

Regroup the ones.

[ 10 ] ones = [ 1 ] ten [ 0 ] ones

Then add the tens.

[ 1 ] ten + [ 1 ] ten = [ 2 ] tens

**b**

```
   3   1
+      9
   4   0
```

**c**

```
   2   5
+      7
   3   2
```

**d**

```
   2   9
+      6
   3   5
```

**e**

```
   3   5
+      8
   4   3
```

44

**66**    **Unit 12:** Numbers to 40

## Additional activity

Ask pupils to work in pairs.

Pupil A calls out two 2-digit numbers less than or equal to 40. The sum of the ones digits should be greater than or equal to 10. Pupil B uses any method of their choice to add the two numbers.

Pupils A and B swap roles.

**5** 14 + 18 = ?

Use a place value chart.

14 = 1 ten 4 ones
18 = 1 ten 8 ones

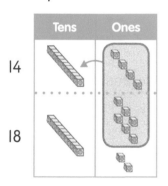

First add the ones.

Tens   Ones

|   | Tens | Ones |
|---|------|------|
|   | 1    | 4    |
| + | 1    | 8    |
|   |      | 2    |

4 ones + 8 ones = 12 ones

Regroup the ones.

12 ones = 1 ten 2 ones

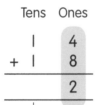

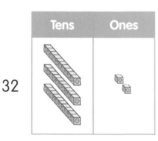

Then add the tens.

Tens   Ones

|   | Tens | Ones |
|---|------|------|
|   | 1    | 4    |
| + | 1    | 8    |
|   | 3    | 2    |

1 ten + 1 ten + 1 ten = 3 tens

14 + 18 = 32

## Teaching sequence

**5**

- Introduce and explain the vertical addition strategy with the help of a place value chart. Notice that regrouping is needed in this section. Show and explain the following strategy using vertical addition:

  **Step 1**: Add the ones.
  4 ones from 14 and 8 ones from 18 make 12 ones.
  12 ones = 1 ten and 2 ones after regrouping.
  Write 2 ones in the ones column, then write 1 ten in the tens column.

  **Step 2**: Add the tens.
  1 ten from 14, 1 ten from 18 and 1 ten (regrouped from ones) make 3.
  Write the result in the tens column. The result is 3 tens and 2 ones which is 32.

**Additional activity**

Ask pupils to repeat the 'Additional activity' from the previous page and to write the numbers in vertical addition format.

**Independent work**

Practice 5 in Practice Book IC, pp 55 to 58.

## Teaching sequence

- Look for pupils who can add a I-digit number to a 2-digit number by regrouping using vertical addition with a place value chart.
- Encourage pupils who need additional support to use concrete materials such as cubes.

---

**Unit 12** Numbers to 40

**6** Add and regroup the numbers.

**a**

| Tens | Ones |
|------|------|
| 1 | 5 |
| + 1 | 6 |
| 3 | 1 |

First add the ones.

[ 5 ] ones + [ 6 ] ones = [ 11 ] ones

Regroup the ones.

[ 11 ] ones = [ 1 ] ten [ 1 ] one

Then add the tens.

[ 1 ] ten + [ 1 ] ten + [ 1 ] ten

= [ 3 ] tens

**b**

```
    1   5
+   1   5
────────────
    3   0
```

**c**

```
    2   2
+   2   8
────────────
    5   0
```

**d**

```
    1   2
+   1   9
────────────
    3   1
```

**e**

```
    1   7
+   1   7
────────────
    3   4
```

Practice Book IC, p.55

46

# Learning objectives: Simple subtraction

**Pupils will be able to:**

- subtract a 1-digit number from a 2-digit number without regrouping
- subtract a 2-digit number from another 2-digit number without regrouping
- use the 'counting back' strategy to subtract
- use the 'taking away' strategy to subtract
- use the number bond strategy to subtract

# Key concept

'Taking away' concept is used in subtraction.

# Thinking skill

Analysing parts and whole

# What you will need

Base ten equipment

---

## Let's Learn!

**Simple subtraction**

**1** 27 − 4 = ?

**a** Count back from 27.

There are different ways to get the answer.

27, **26, 25, 24, 23**

**b** Use a place value chart.

| Tens | Ones |
|------|------|
| 27 | |

First subtract the ones.

| Tens | Ones |
|------|------|
| 2 | 7 |
| − | 4 |
| | 3 |

7 ones − 4 ones = 3 ones

| Tens | Ones |
|------|------|
| 23 | |

Then subtract the tens.

| Tens | Ones |
|------|------|
| 2 | 7 |
| − | 4 |
| 2 | 3 |

2 tens − 0 tens = 2 tens

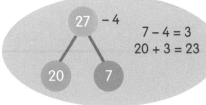

27 − 4
20   7

7 − 4 = 3
20 + 3 = 23

27 − 4 = 23

47

---

# Teaching sequence

**1**

**a**

- Introduce and explain the 'counting back' strategy with the help of a number track or number line.
- Explain to pupils that this strategy is efficient only when the 1-digit is small, just as it is in this question.

**b**

- Introduce and explain the vertical subtraction strategy with the help of a place value chart. Notice that no regrouping is needed in this section. Show and explain the following strategy using vertical subtraction:

  **Step 1**: Subtract the ones. 4 ones are subtracted from 7 ones. Write the result in the ones column.

  **Step 2**: Subtract the tens. 0 tens is subtracted from 2 tens. Write the result in the tens column. The result is 2 tens and 3 ones which is 23.

- You can relate number bonds to this problem and subtract the corresponding tens and ones. E.g. 27 = 2 tens and 7 ones 2 tens − 0 tens = 2 tens 7 ones − 4 ones = 3 ones So combining them the result is 2 tens and 3 ones which is 23.

**Additional activity**

Ask pupils to work in pairs.

Pupil A calls out two numbers: one 2-digit number less than or equal to 40 and a 1-digit number. The ones digits should not require regrouping in subtraction. Pupil B uses any method of their choice to subtract the two numbers.

Pupils A and B swap roles.

## Teaching sequence

- Look for pupils who can apply the 3 strategies in subtracting a 1-digit number from a 2-digit number without regrouping.
  ○ 'Counting back' method
  ○ Vertical subtraction with a place value chart
  ○ Using number bonds
- Explain to pupils that they can use any of these strategies to solve the problem.
- For pupils who need additional support, ask them to use cubes or counters to make number bond pairs.

---

**Unit 12** Numbers to 40

 36 − 3 = ?

**a** Count back from 36.

36, 35, 34, 33

**b** Use a place value chart.

| Tens | Ones |
|------|------|
|      |      |

36

| Tens | Ones |
|------|------|
|      |      |

33

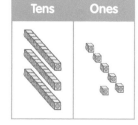

First subtract the ones.
Then subtract the tens.

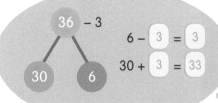

36 − 3 = 33

48

## Additional activity

Ask pupils to work in pairs to write down all possible subtraction sentences using 10, 20, 30 or 40. Then ask them to find all the answers using any subtraction method.

 30 − 20 = ?

**a** Count back from 30.

 30, … 20 , … 10

**b** Use a place value chart.

| Tens | Ones |
|------|------|
| 30 | |

First subtract the ones. Then subtract the tens.

| Tens | Ones |
|------|------|
| 10 | |

Tens Ones
```
   3   0
 − 2   0
 ─────────
   1   0
```

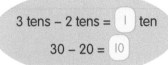 3 tens − 2 tens = 1 ten

30 − 20 = 10

30 − 20 = 10

---

## Teaching sequence

**3**

- Ask pupils to work on the problem first, then explain the steps.

**a**

- Demonstrate the 'counting back' strategy with the help of a number track or number line. Explain to pupils the steps to subtract numbers:

  **Step 1**: 'Counting back' by tens. E.g. 30, …, 20, …10

  **Step 2**: 'Counting back' by ones.

- Encourage pupils to say and practise the strategy.

**b**

- Explain the vertical subtraction strategy, using a place value chart. Notice that no regrouping is needed in this section. Show and explain the following strategy using vertical subtraction:

  **Step 1**: Subtract the ones. As both ones are zero, the result is 0 ones. Write the result in the ones column.

  **Step 2**: Subtract the tens. 2 tens from 20 is subtracted from 3 tens from 30. Write the result in the tens column. The result is 1 ten which is 10.

- Encourage pupils to recall number bonds and use the strategy to subtract the corresponding tens and ones.
- Explain the vertical subtraction strategy, using a place value chart. Notice that no regrouping is needed in this section. Show and explain the following strategy using vertical subtraction:

**Step 1**: Subtract the ones. 0 ones subtracted from 8 ones is 8 ones.
Write the result in the ones column.

**Step 2**: Subtract the tens. 2 tens from 20 is subtracted from 3 tens from 38.
Write the result in the tens column.
The result is 1 ten 8 ones which is 18.

---

**Additional activity**

Ask pupils to work in pairs.

Pupil A calls out two numbers: one 2-digit number less than or equal to 40 and a tens number. Pupil B uses any method of their choice to subtract the tens from the 2-digit number.

Pupils A and B swap roles.

---

Unit 12  Numbers to 40

 38 − 20 = ?

Use a place value chart.

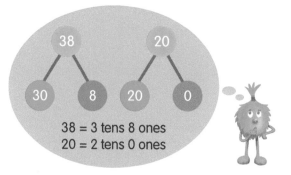

38 = 3 tens 8 ones
20 = 2 tens 0 ones

| Tens | Ones |
|---|---|
| 38 | |

First subtract the ones.

```
  Tens  Ones
    3     8
−   2     0
  ─────────
          8
```

8 ones − 0 ones = 8 ones

| Tens | Ones |
|---|---|
| 18 | |

Then subtract the tens.

```
  Tens  Ones
    3     8
−   2     0
  ─────────
    1     8
```

3 tens − 2 tens = 1 ten

38 − 20 = 18

50

## Additional activity

Ask pupils to work in pairs.

Pupil A calls out two 2-digit numbers less than or equal to 40. The ones digits should not require regrouping in subtraction. Pupil B uses any method of their choice to subtract the two numbers.

Pupils A and B swap roles.

## Independent work

Practice 6 in Practice Book IC, pp 59 to 62.

## Teaching sequence

**5**

- Look for pupils who can apply the vertical subtraction strategy or the number bond method to subtract tens from a 2-digit number without regrouping or counting back in tens.

- Explain to pupils that they can use any of these strategies to solve the problem.

**5** 39 – 22 = ?

39 — 30, ?

22 — ?, 2

39 = 3 tens [9] ones

22 = [2] tens 2 ones

| Tens | Ones |
|------|------|

39

First subtract the ones.
Then subtract the tens.

| Tens | Ones |
|------|------|

[17]

```
Tens  Ones
  3    9
– 2    2
─────────
  1    7
─────────
```

39 – 22 = [17]

Practice Book IC, p.59

51

## Learning objectives: More subtraction

**Pupils will be able to:**

- subtract a 1-digit number from a 2-digit number with regrouping
- subtract a 2-digit number from another 2-digit number with regrouping
- apply the regrouping concept in subtraction
- use the number bond strategy to subtract

## Key concept

The 'taking away' concept is used in subtraction.

## Thinking skills

- Analysing parts and whole
- Comparing (numbers)

## What you will need

- 4 red counters and 20 green counters for each player
- Dice
- Place value chart for each player (see Photocopy master 1 on page 283)

## Teaching sequence

### ① Game

- Introduce this game to prepare pupils for the regrouping process using concrete representation in subtraction. This helps pupils to link the concept to regrouping in subtraction in the following section.
- Explain regrouping before pupils begin the game.

  E.g. Pupils have to do 'trading' when they do not have enough counters to subtract. They need to regroup 1 ten to 10 ones if necessary.

### ②

- Look for pupils who can carry out regrouping from tens to ones. Use the examples below if necessary:

  34 = 3 tens 4 ones
  
  = 2 tens _____ ones
  
  29 = 2 tens 9 ones
  
  = 1 ten _____ ones

---

### Let's Learn!

**More subtraction**

### Game

**Players: 2 to 4**
**You will need:**
- 4 red counters, 20 green counters and a place value chart for each player
- a dice

① **Race to 0!**

How to play:

1  Red counters stand for tens. Green counters stand for ones.

2  Put 4 red counters on your chart.

3  Swap 1 red counter for 10 green counters. Then roll the dice.

4  Take away this number of green counters from your chart. Players take turns to roll the dice and take away.

> The first player to take away all the counters or get 0 wins!

② Regroup the ones into tens and ones. Use counters to help you.

| 25 = | Tens | Ones | = | Tens | Ones |
|---|---|---|---|---|---|
|  | 2 | 5 |  | 1 | 15 |

52

---

## Additional activities

- Ask pupils to complete these subtraction sentences before starting .

  11 − 8 = ___

  12 − 5 = ___

  15 − 8 = ___

  Encourage pupils to use the number bond strategy or recall the addition bonds in addition.

- Ask pupils to work in pairs.

  Pupil A calls out two numbers: a 2-digit number less than or equal to 40 and a 1-digit number. The ones digits should require regrouping in subtraction, i.e. the ones digit of the 2-digit number must be smaller than the 1-digit number. Pupil B uses any method of their choice to subtract the two numbers.

  Pupils A and B swap roles.

## What you will need

- Base ten equipment

---

**3** 32 − 9 = ?

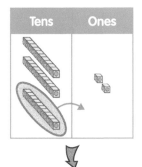

32

First subtract the ones. We can't subtract 9 ones from 2 ones, so we regroup the tens and ones in 32.

Regroup the tens in 32.

3 tens = 2 tens 10 ones

First subtract the ones.

|  | Tens | Ones |
|---|---|---|
|  | ²3 | ¹2 |
| − |  | 9 |
|  |  | 3 |

12 ones − 9 ones = 3 ones

Then subtract the tens.

|  | Tens | Ones |
|---|---|---|
|  | ²3 | ¹2 |
| − |  | 9 |
|  | 2 | 3 |

2 tens − 0 tens = 2 tens

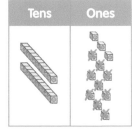

23

32 − 9 = 23

## Teaching sequence

**3**

- Demonstrate the regrouping of 32 to 2 tens and 12 ones with concrete representation.

- Introduce and explain the vertical subtraction strategy with the help of a place value chart. Notice that regrouping is needed in this section. Show and explain the following strategy using vertical subtraction:

  **Step 1**: Subtract the ones. Show the regrouping process, then subtract vertically.
  12 ones − 9 ones = 3 ones
  Write the result in the ones column.

  **Step 2**: Subtract the tens.
  2 tens − 0 tens = 2 tens
  Write the result in the tens column.
  The result is 2 tens and 3 ones which is 23.

53

## Teaching sequence

- Look for pupils who can apply vertical subtraction in subtracting a 1-digit number from a 2-digit number by regrouping.

**a**

- Reinforce the regrouping concept using this example and emphasise the regrouping from tens to ones.

**b** and **c**

- Relate this to number bonds and ask pupils to do the regrouping. Then relate subtraction of ones and tens correspondingly.

---

**Unit 12** Numbers to 40

**4** Subtract the numbers.

**a**

```
  Tens  Ones
    2    6
  –      7
  _____
  | 1 |  9 |
  _____
```

Regroup the tens in 26.

26 = 2 tens [ 6 ] ones

= 1 ten [ 16 ] ones

First subtract the ones.

[ 16 ] ones – [ 7 ] ones = [ 9 ] ones

Then subtract the tens.

[ 1 ] ten – [ 0 ] tens = [ 1 ] ten

**b**

```
  Tens  Ones
    2    3
  –      6
  _____
  | 1 |  7 |
  _____
```

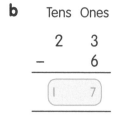
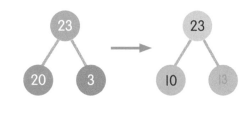

**c**

```
  Tens  Ones
    3    2
  –      8
  _____
  | 2 |  4 |
  _____
```

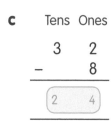
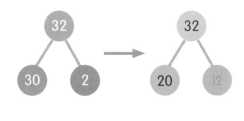

54

## Additional activities

- Ask pupils to complete these subtraction sentences before starting **5**.

  10 − 4 = ___

  10 − 7 = ___

  10 − 9 = ___

  10 − 3 = ___

  Encourage pupils to use the number bond strategy or recall the addition bonds in addition.

- Ask pupils to work in pairs. Pupil A calls out two 2-digit numbers less than or equal to 40. The tens and ones digits of the first number should require regrouping in subtraction. Pupil B uses any method of their choice to subtract the two numbers.

  Pupils A and B swap roles.

## What you will need

- Base ten equipment

## Teaching sequence

**5**

- Explain the subtraction procedure using strategy similar to **4**.
- Emphasise the regrouping procedure using concrete representation:

  40 = 4 tens 0 ones
  = 3 tens 10 ones

---

**5** 40 − 29 = ?

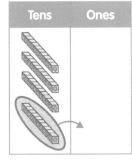

40

First subtract the ones. We can't subtract 9 ones from 0 ones, so we regroup the tens and ones in 40.

Regroup the tens in 40.

4 tens = 3 tens 10 ones

First subtract the ones.

```
Tens  Ones
  ³4   ¹0
−  2    9
─────────
         1
```

10 ones − 9 ones = 1 one

Then subtract the tens.

```
Tens  Ones
  ³4   ¹0
−  2    9
─────────
   1    1
```

3 tens − 2 tens = 1 ten

||

40 − 29 = 11

55

## Independent work

Practice 7 in Practice Book IC,
pp 63 to 66.

## Teaching sequence

- Look for pupils who can
  apply vertical subtraction in
  subtracting a I-digit number
  from a 2-digit number with
  regrouping.

**a**

- Reinforce the regrouping
  concept using this example
  and emphasise on regrouping
  from tens to ones.

**b** and **c**

- Relate this to number bonds
  and ask pupils to do the
  regrouping. Then relate
  subtraction of ones and tens
  correspondingly.

---

**Unit I2** Numbers to 40

**6** Regroup and subtract the numbers.

**a**

| Tens | Ones |
|------|------|
| 3 | 4 |
| – I | 5 |
| I | 9 |

Regroup the tens in 34.
34 = 3 tens ⟨ 4 ⟩ ones
  = 2 tens ⟨ I4 ⟩ ones

First subtract the ones.
⟨ I4 ⟩ ones – ⟨ 5 ⟩ ones = ⟨ 9 ⟩ ones

Then subtract the tens.
⟨ 2 ⟩ tens – ⟨ I ⟩ ten = ⟨ I ⟩ ten

**b**

| Tens | Ones |
|------|------|
| 3 | I |
| – I | 9 |
| I | 2 |

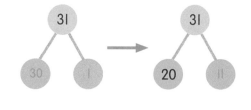

**c**

| Tens | Ones |
|------|------|
| 3 | 5 |
| – 2 | 8 |
| | 7 |

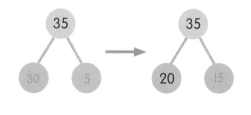

Practice Book IC, p.63

56

## Learning objectives: Adding three numbers

**Pupils will be able to:**

- add three 1-digit numbers to 40
- use the number bond strategy to add
- apply the 'making ten' strategy to add

## Key concept

- 'Add on' and 'making ten' concepts are used in adding three numbers
- The regrouping concept is also applied

## Thinking skills

- Analysing parts and whole
- Comparing (numbers)

## What you will need

Cubes

---

## Let's Learn!

### Adding three numbers

**1** $5 + 7 + 6 = ?$

**a**

$5 + 7 + 6$

Step 1    5   2

10

Make 10 first.
$5 + 5 = 10$

Step 2    $2 + 6 = 8$

Step 3    $10 + 8 = 18$

$5 + 7 + 6 = 18$
or

**b**      $5 + 7 + 6$

Step 1    3   3

10

Make 10 first.
$7 + 3 = 10$

Step 2    $5 + 3 = 8$

Step 3    $10 + 8 = 18$

$5 + 7 + 6 = 18$

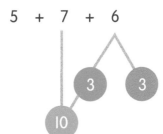

57

---

## Teaching sequence

**1**

- Explain and demonstrate the procedures of adding three 1-digit numbers using number bonds.
- Emphasise the basic principle is to make ten and another number from the given set of 2 numbers.
- Revise addition of 2 numbers using number bonds:

**a** $5 + 7 = ?$

Show the number bond:
5-2—7

Therefore:
$5 + 7 = 5 + 5 + 2 = 10 + 2$

**b** $7 + 6 = ?$

Show the number bond:
3-3—6

Therefore:
$7 + 6 = 7 + 3 + 3 = 10 + 3$

- Then work through the two different addition methods in the textbook.

## Independent work

Practice 8 in Practice Book IC,
pp 67 to 70.

## Teaching sequence

**2** and **3**

- Look for pupils who can apply the number bond strategy in adding three I-digit numbers.
- If necessary, remind pupils to use number bonds that will lead to I0 plus another number.

**4** *Let's Explore!*

- Ask pupils to work in groups.
- Encourage pupils to discover different ways of adding 3 numbers by using different combinations of any two numbers.
- Encourage groups to share their answers and discuss these with the class.

**Unit 12** Numbers to 40

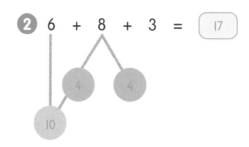

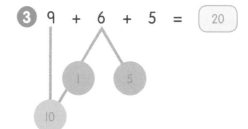

Practice Book IC, p.67

### Let's Explore!

**4** Show two ways to add the three numbers.

$9 + 7 + 8 = \boxed{\phantom{00}}$

Use number bonds to make tens.

$10 + 10 = 20$
$20 + 4 = 24$

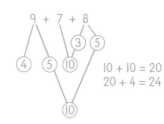

$10 + 10 = 20$
$20 + 4 = 24$

58

## Learning objectives: Solving word problems

**Pupils will be able to:**

- solve I-step word problems in addition or subtraction
- apply the following concepts in addition: 'part-whole', 'adding on' and 'comparing'
- apply the following concepts in subtraction: 'part-whole', 'taking away' and 'comparing'

## Key concept

The 'part-whole', 'taking away', 'adding on' and 'comparing' concepts are used to solve word problems involving addition and subtraction.

## Thinking skills

- Analysing parts and whole
- Comparing (numbers)

## What you will need

Cubes

---

# Let's Learn!

### Solving word problems

**1** Peter has 15 .
Miya has 3 more  than Peter.
How many  does Miya have?

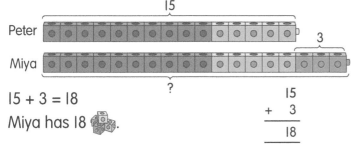

15 + 3 = 18
Miya has 18 .

$$\begin{array}{r} 15 \\ +\phantom{0}3 \\ \hline 18 \end{array}$$

**2** Liam pours 10 glasses of orange squash.
Emma pours 8 more glasses of orange squash than Liam.
How many glasses of orange squash does Emma pour?

We can use  to show the number of glasses of orange squash.

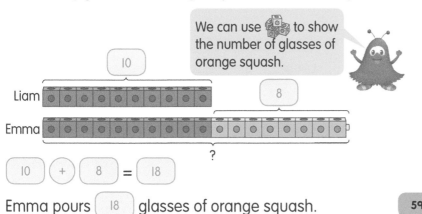

10 + 8 = 18

Emma pours 18 glasses of orange squash.

59

---

## Teaching sequence

**1**

- Note that this question applies the 'comparing' concept in addition.
- Use cubes to demonstrate the problem to pupils.
- Show that Peter has a set of 15 cubes, then show that Miya has another set of cubes which is 3 more than Peter's set of cubes.
- Place the smaller set of cubes above the other for a clearer visual comparison.
- Point out that 3 more than 15 means: 15 + 3 = 18

**2**

- Look for pupils who can solve a similar problem. Give pupils cubes to work with.
- Ask pupils to read the problem and then to use cubes to model the word problem statements.
- Then ask them to work out unknown values to complete the solution.

Ask pupils to work in pairs.
Show the following model:

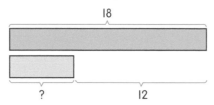

Ask them to look at the model
and to write an addition story
based on the model.

## Teaching sequence

- Note that this question applies
  the 'comparing' concept in
  subtraction.
- Use cubes to demonstrate the
  problem to pupils.
- Show that Hardeep has a set
  of 14 cubes and that it is 11
  cubes more than Ruby's set of
  cubes.
- Place the smaller set of cubes
  below the other for a clearer
  visual comparison.
- Point out that 11 less than 14
  is 3.
- Explain to pupils that this is a
  subtraction problem and not
  an addition problem although
  the term 'more' is used in the
  question.

- Look for pupils who can solve
  a similar problem. Give pupils
  cubes to work with.
- Ask pupils to read the
  problem and to use cubes
  to model the word problem
  statements.
- Then ask them to work out the
  unknown values to complete
  the solution.

---

**Unit 12** Numbers to 40

3 Hardeep lives at number 14 Green Lane.
His house number is 11 more than Ruby's.
What is Ruby's house number?

We can use 🎲 to show
the house numbers.

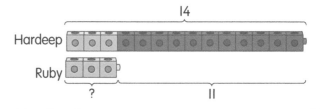

$14 - 11 = 3$

Ruby lives at number 3.

$$\begin{array}{r} 14 \\ -\ 11 \\ \hline 3 \end{array}$$

4 Ben makes 20 cakes for a party.
He makes 6 more cakes than Nick.
How many cakes does Nick make?

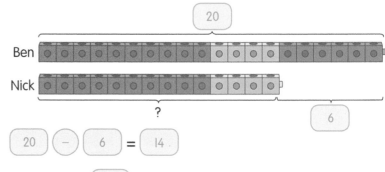

20 − 6 = 14

Nick makes 14 cakes.

60

## Additional activity

Ask pupils to work in pairs.
Show the following model:

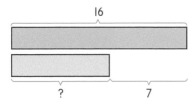

Ask them to look at the model
and to write a subtraction story
based on the model.

**5** Millie has 19 marbles.
Anna has 7 fewer marbles than Millie.
How many marbles does Anna have?

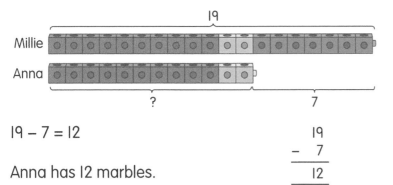

$19 - 7 = 12$

$$\begin{array}{r} 19 \\ -\phantom{0}7 \\ \hline 12 \end{array}$$

Anna has 12 marbles.

**6** Amy has 16 stickers.
Serge has 7 fewer stickers than Amy.
How many stickers does Serge have?

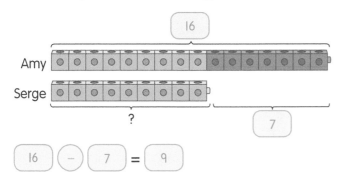

$\boxed{16} \; \boxed{-} \; \boxed{7} \; \boxed{=} \; \boxed{9}$

Serge has $\boxed{9}$ stickers.

61

## Teaching sequence

**5**

- Note that this problem applies the 'comparing' concept in subtraction.
- Explain to pupils that the key word for this problem is 'fewer' than, whereas in **3**, the key word is 'more' than. Although the key words are different, both questions are concerned with subtraction.
- Use cubes to demonstrate the problem to pupils.
- Show that Millie has 19 cubes representing marbles and Anna has another set that has 7 fewer marbles than Millie's set.
- Point out that 7 less than 19 is 12.

**6**

- Look for pupils who can solve a similar problem. Give pupils cubes to work with.
- Ask pupils to read the problem and to use cubes to model the word problem statements.
- Then ask them to work out the unknown values to complete the solution.

## Objective of activity

Pupils will be able to apply and use number bonds to 40 to make number sentences.

## Thinking skill

Analysing parts and whole

## Independent work

Practice 9, *Challenging Practice, Problem Solving* and Review 4 in Practice Book IC, pp 7I to 80.

## Teaching sequence

**7**

- Ask pairs of pupils to create addition and subtraction stories using the 'comparing' concepts covered earlier.

**a**

E.g. Addition story:
Jack collects 24 sea shells. Ruby collects 7 more sea shells than Jack. How many sea shells does Ruby collect?

E.g. Subtraction story:
Jack collects 24 sea shells. He collects 7 more sea shells than Ruby. How many sea shells does Ruby collect?

**b**

E.g. Addition story:
Bella makes I0 sandwiches. She makes 7 sandwiches less than Tom. How many sandwiches does Tom make?

E.g. Subtraction story:
Bella makes I0 sandwiches. Tom makes 7 sandwiches less than Bella. How many sandwiches does Tom make?

**8** *Put On Your Thinking Caps!*

- One strategy is to think of two numbers that make 9 or I0.
- Then find the third number.
  $7 + 3 = 10$ and $10 + 2 = 12$
  So 2, 3, 7 make I2.
  $6 + 4 = 10$ and $10 + 2 = 12$
  So 2, 4, 6 make I2.
  $4 + 5 = 9$ and $9 + 3 = 12$
  So 3, 4, 5 make I2.

---

## Activity

**7** Work in pairs.

**a** Write one addition story and one subtraction story. Use the following words to help you.

| Jack | Miya | more than |
| sea shells | how many | collects |

**b** Write one addition story and one subtraction story. Use the following words to help you.

| Bella | Tom | less than |
| sandwiches | how many | makes |

Practice Book IC, p.7I

## Put On Your Thinking Caps!

**8** Pick any three numbers shown below and complete the addition sentences.
You can only use a number once in each sentence.

( 2 ) ( 3 ) ( 4 ) ( 5 ) ( 6 ) ( 7 )

[ 2 ] + [ 3 ] + [ 7 ] = I2

[ 2 ] + [ 4 ] + [ 6 ] = I2

Practice Book IC, p.73

[ 3 ] + [ 4 ] + [ 5 ] = I2

Practice Book IC, p.74

62

# Unit 12 Numbers to 40

Date: _____

## Practice 1    Counting to 40

1 Make tens, then count on.
Fill in the missing numbers.

**Example**

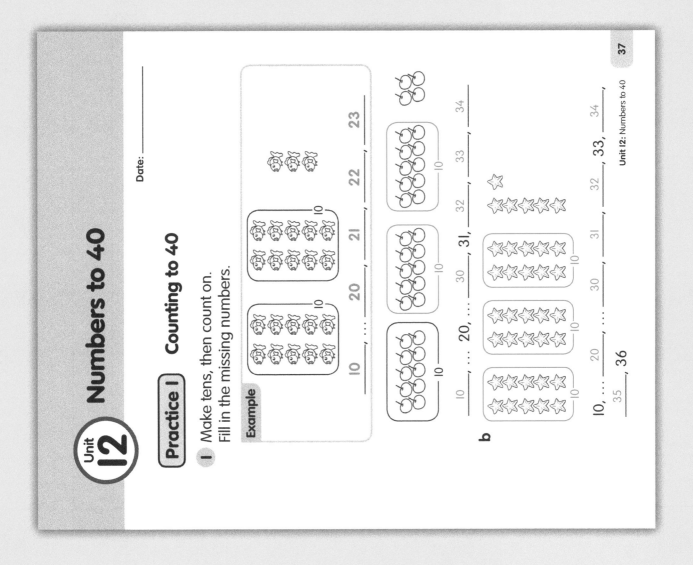

10 ___ 20 21 22 23

10 ___, ___, 20, ___, 30, 31, ___, 32, 33, 34

b

10, ___, 20, ___, 30, ___, 31, 32, 33, 34

___, 35 ___, 36

**2** Circle groups of 10.
Then count on and write the numbers.

a 28

b 35

c 39

d 26

e 25

**3** How many ◇ are there?

a 23

b 30

c 34

d 40

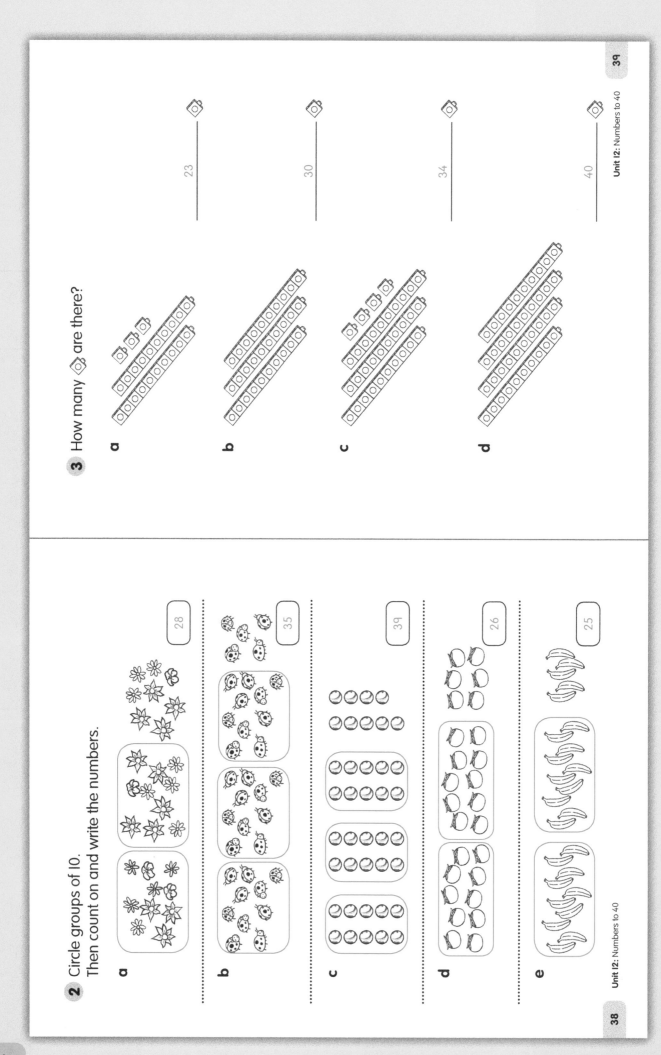

Practice 2  Place value

1 What are the missing numbers?

a

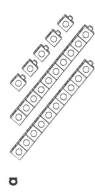

25 = 2 tens 5 ones

b

37 = 3 tens 7 ones

4 Write the numbers.

a twenty-five 25          b twenty-seven 27

c thirty-nine 39          d thirty-two 32

e thirty-four 34          f twenty-nine 29

5 Write the numbers in words.

a 21 twenty-one           b 26 twenty-six

c 37 thirty-seven         d 22 twenty-two

e 40 forty                f 33 thirty-three

g 28 twenty-eight         h 36 thirty-six

i 35 thirty-five          j 31 thirty-one

6 Fill in the missing numbers.

a 8 + 30 = 38

b 20 + 3 = 23

c 30 + 9 = 39

d 30 and 2 make 32.

e 30 and 5 make 35.

f 7 and 20 make 27.

g 20 and 8 make 28.

h 30 and 6 make 36.

## 3

Count in tens and ones.
Fill in the missing numbers in the place value charts
and then fill in the spaces.

**Example**

| Tens | Ones |
|---|---|
| 2 | 3 |

$23 = \underline{2}$ tens $\underline{3}$ ones

$20 + 3 = \underline{23}$

**a**

| Tens | Ones |
|---|---|
| 2 | 6 |

$26 = \underline{2}$ tens $\underline{6}$ ones

$20 + 6 = \underline{26}$

## 2

What number does each place value chart show?
Fill in the spaces.

**a**

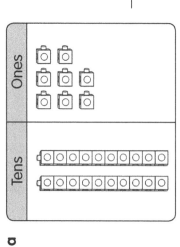

| Tens | Ones |
|---|---|

$\underline{28}$

**b**

| Tens | Ones |
|---|---|

$\underline{39}$

**Practice 3** Comparing, order and pattern

1 Fill in the missing numbers.

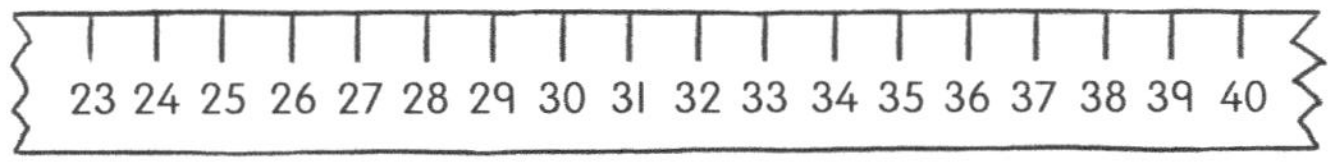

23 24 25 26 27 28 29 30 31 32 33 34 35 36 37 38 39 40

a 1 more than 23 is __24__.

b 1 more than 29 is __30__.

c 1 less than 35 is __34__.

d 2 more than 19 is __21__.

e 2 more than 26 is __28__.

f 2 less than 31 is __29__.

g 3 more than 27 is __30__.

h 3 more than 36 is __39__.

i 3 less than 25 is __22__.

j 3 less than 40 is __37__.

k __29__ is 2 more than 27.

l __24__ is 2 less than 26.

m __33__ is 3 more than 30.

n __27__ is 3 less than 30.

o __37__ is 2 more than 35.

p __33__ is 2 less than 35.

b

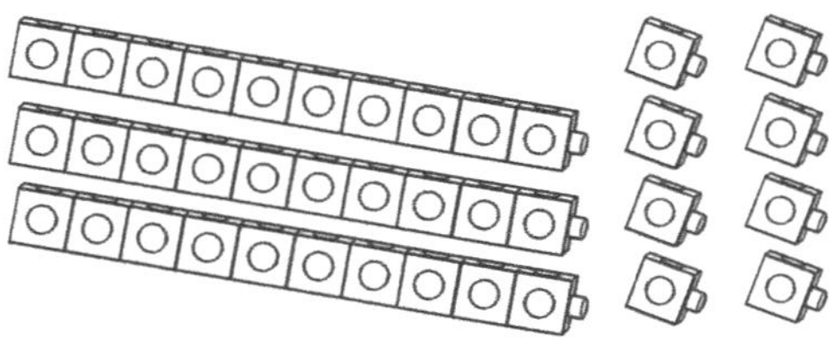

| Tens | Ones |
|------|------|
| 3 | 8 |

38 = __3__ tens __8__ ones

30 + 8 = __38__

c

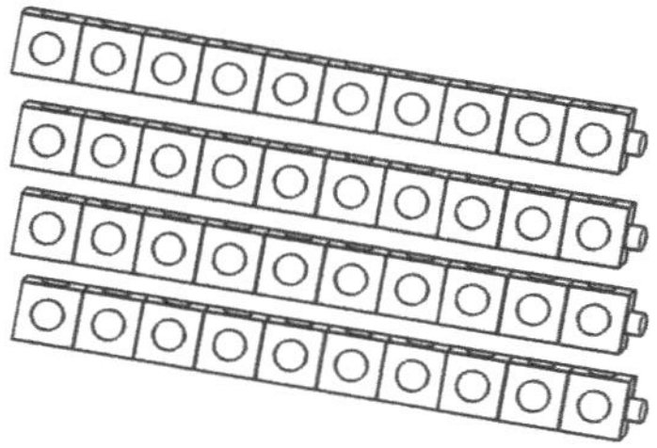

| Tens | Ones |
|------|------|
| 4 | 0 |

40 = __4__ tens __0__ ones

40 + 0 = __40__

**2** Count the number in each set.
One bundle stands for 10 lolly sticks.

**a**

Set A

Set B

Which set has more lolly sticks?
Set __A__ has more lolly sticks.

Which number is greater?
__32__ is greater than __29__ .

**b**

Set A

Set B

Which set has fewer lolly sticks?
Set __B__ has fewer lolly sticks.

Which number is smaller?
__24__ is smaller than __36__ .

---

**3  a** Which number is greater?
Circle it.

(32) or 23

37 or (39)

**b** Which number is smaller?
Circle it.

32 or (28)

(38) or 40

**4** Compare the numbers.
Then fill in the spaces.

34    39    37

__34__ is the smallest.

__39__ is the greatest.

**5** Arrange the numbers in order.
Begin with the smallest number.

36    24    32

__24__ , __32__ , __36__
smallest

**6** Use the numbers below to fill in the spaces.

**a**

| 23 | 38 | 35 | 27 |
|----|----|----|----|

_23_ is less than 27.

_38_ is greater than 35.

35 is greater than _23_ and _27_ but less than _38_.

The smallest number is _23_.

The greatest number is _38_.

**b**

| 40 | 24 | 39 | 26 |
|----|----|----|----|

_26_ is 2 more than 24.

_39_ is 1 less than 40.

_26_ is less than 39 but greater than 24.

The smallest number is _24_.

The greatest number is _40_.

---

**7** Complete the number patterns.

**a** 18, 19, _20_, 21, _22_, 23, _24_

**b** 30, 31, 32, _33_, 34, _35_, _36_

**c** _28_, _29_, 30, 31, _32_, 33, 34

**d** 33, _32_, 31, _30_, _29_, 28, 27

**e** 30, 32, _34_, 36, 38, _40_

**f** 27, _25_, _23_, 21, 19, 17, 15

**g** _20_, 23, 26, 29, _32_, 35

**h** 33, _30_, _27_, 24, 21, _18_

**i** _0_, 10, _20_, 30, 40

Date: _____

## Practice 4    Simple addition

1 Add by counting on.

a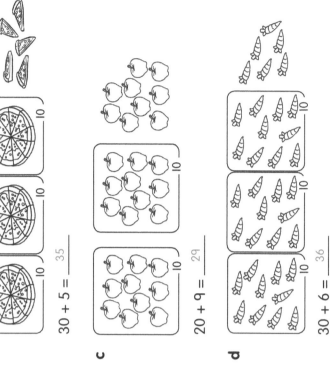

20 + 3 = _23_

b

30 + 5 = _35_

c

30 + 5 = _35_

c

20 + 9 = _29_

d

30 + 6 = _36_

---

8 Millie's ball falls into a number machine.
Which ball is it?
Write the correct number in the ○.

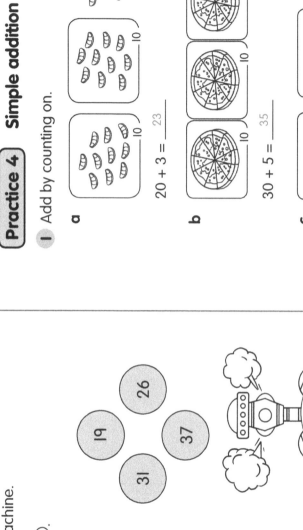

26   19   37   31

3 more than the number on Millie's ball

In   19

Out

22

**3** Complete the place value charts.
Then add the numbers.

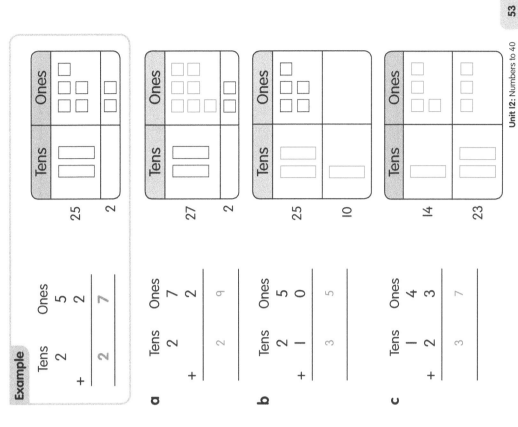

**Example**

| Tens | Ones |
|------|------|
| 2 | 5 |
| + | 2 |
| **2** | **7** |

**a**

| Tens | Ones |
|------|------|
| 2 | 7 |
| + | 2 |
| 2 | 9 |

**b**

| Tens | Ones |
|------|------|
| 2 | 5 |
| 1 | 0 |
| + 3 | 5 |

**c**

| Tens | Ones |
|------|------|
| 1 | 4 |
| 2 | 3 |
| + 3 | 7 |

---

**2** Add the numbers.

**Example**

25 + 4 =   2  tens  5  ones + 4 ones

(number bond: 20 and 5)

=  2  tens 9 ones

= 29

**a** 32 + 6 =  3  tens  2  ones + 6 ones

(number bond: 30 and 2)

= 3 tens  8  ones

= 38

**b** 2 + 37 = 2 ones +  3  tens  7  ones

(number bond: 30 and 7)

=  3  tens 9 ones

= 39

**c** 16 + 2 = 18

(number bond: 10 and 6)

**d** 24 + 3 = 27

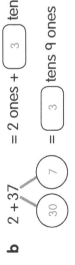

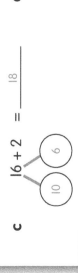

(number bond: 20 and 4)

## Practice 5   More addition

1  Think of tens and ones.
   Then add the numbers.

**Example**

$$23 + 9 = \underline{2}\ \text{tens}\ \underline{3}\ \text{ones} + \underline{9}\ \text{ones}$$
$$= \underline{2}\ \text{tens}\ \underline{12}\ \text{ones}$$
$$= \underline{32}$$

a  $37 + 3 = \underline{3}\ \text{tens}\ \underline{7}\ \text{ones} + \underline{3}\ \text{ones}$
$$= \underline{3}\ \text{tens}\ \underline{10}\ \text{ones}$$
$$= \underline{40}$$

b  $25 + 8 = \underline{2}\ \text{tens}\ \underline{5}\ \text{ones} + \underline{8}\ \text{ones}$
$$= \underline{2}\ \text{tens}\ \underline{13}\ \text{ones}$$
$$= \underline{33}$$

c  $26 + 6 = \underline{2}\ \text{tens}\ \underline{6}\ \text{ones} + \underline{6}\ \text{ones}$
$$= \underline{2}\ \text{tens}\ \underline{12}\ \text{ones}$$
$$= \underline{32}$$

---

4  Add the numbers.

a
```
   2 5
 +   4
 -----
   2 9
```

b
```
   2 6
 +   2
 -----
   2 8
```

c
```
   2 0
 + 2 0
 -----
   4 0
```

d
```
   4 0
 + 2 4
 -----
   6 4
```

e
```
   2 6
 + 1 3
 -----
   3 9
```

f
```
   1 2
 + 2 7
 -----
   3 9
```

5  Fill in the missing numbers.

a  $25 + 12 = \underline{37}$

[2][5]  [1][2]
+
[3][7]

b  $14 + 24 = \underline{38}$

[1][4]  [2][4]
+
[3][8]

**3** Fill in the missing numbers.

**a** 18 + 7 = __25__
```
      1   8
  +       7
  _____
      2   5
```

**b** 13 + 19 = __32__
```
      1   3
  +   1   9
  _____
      3   2
```

**c** 17 + 16 = __33__
```
      1   7
  +   1   6
  _____
      3   3
```

**d** 8 + 32 = __40__
```
          8
  +   3   2
  _____
      4   0
```

**d** 5 + 29 = __5__ ones + __2__ tens __9__ ones

= __2__ tens __14__ ones

= __34__

**e** 19 + 21 = __1__ ten __9__ ones + __2__ tens __1__ one

= __3__ tens __10__ ones

= __40__

**2** Add the numbers.

**a**
```
    1   8
  +     5
  _____
    2   3
```

**b**
```
    2   4
  +     9
  _____
    3   3
```

**c**
```
    2   5
  +     6
  _____
    3   1
```

**d**
```
    1   6
  +     7
  _____
    2   3
```

**e**
```
    1   6
  + 1   4
  _____
    3   0
```

**f**
```
    2   5
  + 1   5
  _____
    4   0
```

## Practice 6  Simple subtraction

**1** Subtract the numbers by counting back.

**Example**

24 – 2 = _22_

24, 23, 22

a  27 – 6 = _21_

b  35 – 4 = _31_

c  38 – 8 = _30_

d  24 – 3 = _21_

e  27 – 5 = _22_

f  37 – 4 = _33_

g  39 – 4 = _35_

h  39 – 9 = _30_

**2** Fill in the missing numbers.

a  37 – 5 = _3_ tens 7 ones – _5_ ones

    = _3_ tens 2 ones

    = _32_

b  38 – 3 = _3_ tens _8_ ones – 3 ones

    = 3 tens _5_ ones

    = _35_

---

**4** Find the answer to this joke.

What animal falls from the clouds on a rainy day?

A  I  E  N  R  R  D  E

a  14 + 7 = _21_

b  26 + 8 = _34_

c  29 + 6 = _35_

d  25 + 7 = _32_

e  33 + 7 = _40_

f  12 + 28 = _40_

g  24 + 6 = _30_

h  17 + 18 = _35_

| R | A | I | N | – |
|---|---|---|---|---|
| 40 | 21 | 34 | 32 | |

| D | E | E | R |
|---|---|---|---|
| 30 | 35 | 35 | 40 |

## 4 Fill in the missing numbers.

**a** 29 − 26 = 3

| Tens | Ones |
|------|------|
| 2 | 9 |
| 2 | 6 |
| | 3 |

**b** 38 − 10 = 28

| Tens | Ones |
|------|------|
| 3 | 8 |
| 1 | 0 |
| 2 | 8 |

**c** 27 − 17 = 10

| Tens | Ones |
|------|------|
| 2 | 7 |
| 1 | 7 |
| 1 | 0 |

**d** 26 − 5 = 21

| Tens | Ones |
|------|------|
| 2 | 6 |
| | 5 |
| 2 | 1 |

**e** 36 − 5 = 31

| Tens | Ones |
|------|------|
| 3 | 6 |
| | 5 |
| 3 | 1 |

**f** 38 − 8 = 30

| Tens | Ones |
|------|------|
| 3 | 8 |
| | 8 |
| 3 | 0 |

## 3 Subtract the numbers.

**a**

| Tens | Ones |
|------|------|
| 1 | 6 |
| | 2 |
| 1 | 4 |

**b**

| Tens | Ones |
|------|------|
| 2 | 8 |
| | 4 |
| 2 | 4 |

**c**

| Tens | Ones |
|------|------|
| 3 | 5 |
| | 2 |
| 3 | 3 |

**d**

| Tens | Ones |
|------|------|
| 3 | 6 |
| | 6 |
| 3 | 0 |

**e**

| Tens | Ones |
|------|------|
| 4 | 0 |
| 2 | 0 |
| 2 | 0 |

**f**

| Tens | Ones |
|------|------|
| 2 | 3 |
| 1 | 0 |
| 1 | 3 |

**g**

| Tens | Ones |
|------|------|
| 3 | 6 |
| 1 | 1 |
| 2 | 5 |

**h**

| Tens | Ones |
|------|------|
| 3 | 4 |
| 1 | 4 |
| 2 | 0 |

5  Farha puts a ball into a number machine.
Which ball is it?
Write the correct number in the ○.

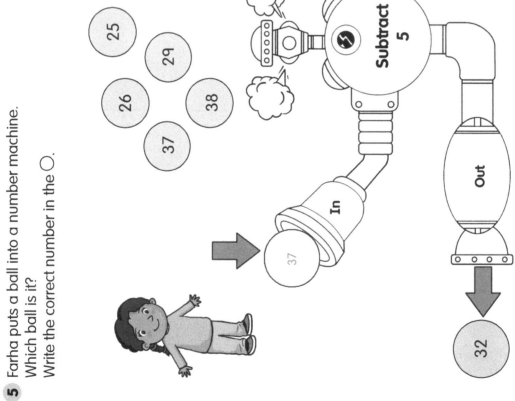

25  29  26  38  37

In: 37

Subtract 5

Out: 32

---

Date: _____

## Practice 7    More subtraction

1  Subtract the numbers.

a
```
   2 3
 –   6
 ─────
   1 7
```

b
```
   2 4
 –   8
 ─────
   1 6
```

c
```
   3 3
 –   5
 ─────
   2 8
```

d
```
   3 6
 –   9
 ─────
   2 7
```

e
```
   2 5
 –   6
 ─────
   1 9
```

f
```
   2 0
 – 1 8
 ─────
     2
```

**2** Fill in the missing numbers.

a  32 − 14 = 18

| 3 | 2 |
|---|---|
|   | 4 |
|   | 8 |

−

b  36 − 7 = 29

| 3 | 6 |
|---|---|
|   | 7 |
| 2 | 9 |

−

c  25 − 18 = 7

| 2 | 5 |
|---|---|
|   | 8 |
|   | 7 |

−

d  31 − 18 = 13

| 3 | 1 |
|---|---|
|   | 8 |
|   | 3 |

−

**3** Find the answer to this joke.

How do you cut the sea?

a  38 − 9 = 29

b  30 − 18 = 12

c  32 − 5 = 27

d  35 − 8 = 27

e  23 − 8 = 15

f  34 − 19 = 15

| S | E | A |
|---|---|---|
| 27 | 12 | 15 |

−

| S | A | W |
|---|---|---|
| 27 | 15 | 29 |

with a

## Practice 8  Adding three numbers

1 Add the numbers.

a

$4 + 5 + 6 =$ 15

b

$8 + 7 + 7 =$ 22

c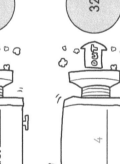

$6 + 9 + 8 =$ 23

d

$5 + 4 + 8 =$ 17

---

4 Peter drops one ball into each number machine.
What happens to the numbers on the balls?
Write the missing numbers.

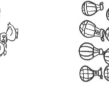

a 33 → Subtract 7 → 26

b 28 → Add 4 → 32

## 2 Make ten. Then add the numbers.

**Example**

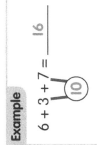

$6 + 3 + 7 = \underline{16}$

$6 + 10 = 16$

**a** $5 + 8 + 5 = \underline{18}$

$10 + 8 = 18$

**b** $8 + 9 + 2 = \underline{19}$

$10 + 9 = 19$

**c** $9 + 7 + 2 = \underline{18}$

$10 + 6 + 2 = 18$

**d** $6 + 6 + 5 = \underline{17}$

$10 + 6 + 1 = 17$

**e** $8 + 8 + 8 = \underline{24}$

$10 + 4 + 10 = 24$

## 3 Add the numbers.

**a** $9 + 4 + 4 = \underline{17}$

**b** $8 + 3 + 1 = \underline{12}$

**c** $7 + 7 + 3 = \underline{17}$

**d** $8 + 8 + 2 = \underline{18}$

**e** $2 + 9 + 5 = \underline{16}$

**f** $6 + 8 + 9 = \underline{23}$

## 4 Fill in the circles with the numbers 0, 2 and 4.
Each ◯—◯—◯ must make 8.
You can only use each number once.

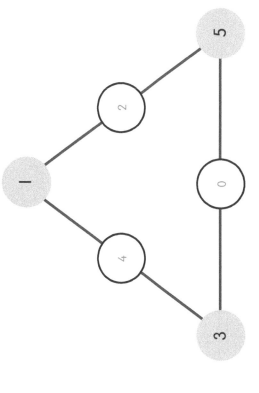

Date: _____

## Practice 9 | Solving word problems

Solve the word problems.

1  Omar has 12 carrots.
Ella has 5 more carrots than Omar.
How many carrots does Ella have?

12 + 5 = 17

Ella has ___17___ carrots.

2  Hardeep buys 15 stickers.
Millie buys 7 fewer stickers than Hardeep.
How many stickers does Millie buy?

15 − 7 = 8

Millie buys ___8___ stickers.

---

5  Ruby puts a ball into the number machine.
What happens to the number on the ball?
Fill in the missing numbers.

Answers vary. Example:

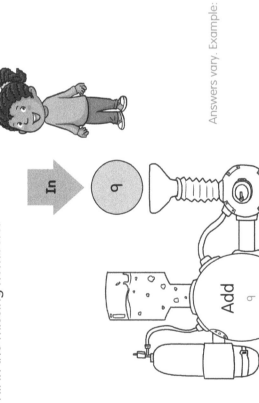

In

9

Add
9

Add
9

Out

27

Add
9

Date: _____

## Challenging Practice

The children are selling tickets.

Miya  Farha        Omar  Ella

Peter

| Name | Number of tickets sold |
|------|------------------------|
| Peter | 16 |
| Farha | 28 |
| Ella | 17 |
| Miya | 23 |
| Omar | 34 |

1 Who sells the most tickets? _____ Omar

2 Who sells fewer tickets than Ella? _____ Peter

3 How many tickets do Peter and Ella sell altogether?

33

4 Which two children sell a total of 40 tickets?

_____ and _____
Ella        Miya

5 Ella wants to sell 1 ticket more than Omar.
How many more tickets does she have to sell?

18

---

3 Miya has 14 toy cars.
She has 9 more toy cars than Jack.
How many toy cars does Jack have?

14 – 9 = 5

Jack has _____ toy cars.
5

4 Peter buys 6 oranges.
He buys 5 fewer oranges than Tai.
How many oranges does Tai buy?

6 + 5 = 11

Tai buys _____ oranges.
11

# Review 4

Date: _____

**1** Fill in the spaces with **heavier than, lighter than** and **as heavy as.**

book

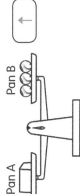
ball    doll    book

The book is ___ as heavy as ___ the ball.

The doll is ___ lighter than ___ the book.

The ball is ___ heavier than ___ than the doll.

**2** Fill in the spaces.

🍪 stands for 1 unit.

Pan A    Pan B

The mass of the box is ___3___ units.

Add 1 marble to Pan A.
Draw ⬇ or ⬆ to show if Pan B goes up or down.   [⬆]

---

## Problem Solving

Date: _____

**1** Ruby, Jack and Millie go to a fair with Jack's mum.

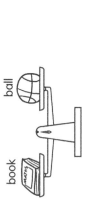

| Fun Rides | |
| --- | --- |
| Roller Coaster | 10 tokens |
| Bumper Car | 7 tokens |
| Flying Elephant | 6 tokens |
| Merry-Go-Round | 5 tokens |

They buy tokens to go on the rides.
What rides do they go on?

**a** Ruby goes on two different rides.
She uses 15 tokens.
Ruby goes on the __Merry-Go-Round__ and the __Roller Coaster__.

**b** Jack goes on two different rides.
He uses 12 tokens.
Jack goes on the __Bumper Car__ and the __Merry-Go-Round__.

**c** Millie goes on three different rides.
She uses 21 tokens.
Millie goes on the __Roller Coaster__, the __Flying Elephant__ and the __Merry-Go-Round__.

**5** The graph shows the number of vehicles in a car park.

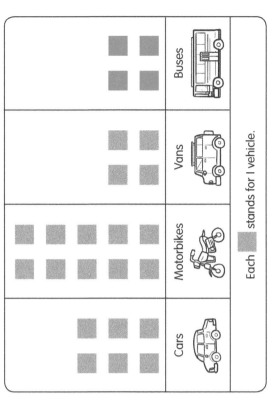

| Cars | Motorbikes | Vans | Buses |
|---|---|---|---|

Each ▢ stands for 1 vehicle.

Look at the graph and work out the answers.

**a** There are ___2___ more cars than vans.

**b** There are ___10___ cars and vans altogether.

**c** There are 2 fewer buses than cars.
Draw ▢ to show the number of buses.

**d** Some motorbikes leave the car park.
Now the number of motorbikes and the number of vans are the same.
___6___ motorbikes leave the car park.

---

**3** Tai brings these things to the beach.

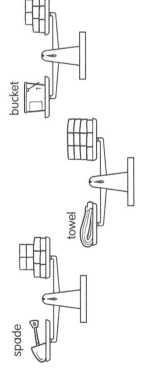

spade        towel        bucket

**a** The spade is lighter than the ___towel___ .

**b** Arrange the objects in order.
Begin with the heaviest.

___towel___    ___spade___    ___bucket___
heaviest

**4** Arrange the bags in order.
Begin with the lightest.

___B___    ___C___    ___A___
lightest

**6** Count the things and write the correct numbers.

a    24

b 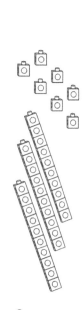   37

**7** Write the numbers.

a twenty-five: ___25___   b thirty: ___30___

**8** Write the numbers in words.

a 37: ___thirty-seven___   b 40: ___forty___

**9** Fill in the spaces.

a Which number is greater?

25 or 17 ___25___   26 or 29 ___29___

b Which number is smaller?

10 or 29 ___10___   38 or 33 ___33___

**10** Look at these numbers: 16, 9, 21, 35

The smallest number is ___9___.

The greatest number is ___35___.

___21___ is less than 35 but more than 16.

Arrange the numbers in order.
Begin with the smallest.

___9___, ___16___, ___21___, ___35___
smallest

**11** Complete the number patterns.

a 17, 20, 23, ___26___, ___29___, 32

b 28, ___32___, ___36___, 40

**12** Fill in the spaces.

a 2 less than 25 is ___23___.

b ___21___ is 3 more than 18.

c 24 = ___2___ tens and 4 ones

d 18 = 1 ten and ___8___ ones

**13** Add or subtract the numbers.

**a** 21 + 7 = _28_

**b** 24 + 10 = _34_

**c** 27 − 3 = _24_

**d** 38 − 15 = _23_

**e** 6 + 3 + 7 = _16_

**f** 9 + 8 + 5 = _22_

**g**
```
   1 4
+  1 7
-----
   3 1
```

**h**
```
   2 3
+  1 6
-----
   3 9
```

**i**
```
   1 8
+  1 7
-----
   3 5
```

**j**
```
   2 9
+  1 1
-----
   4 0
```

**k**
```
   2 1
−  1 7
-----
     4
```

**l**
```
   3 6
−  1 8
-----
   1 8
```

**m**
```
   3 6
−  2 4
-----
   1 2
```

**n**
```
   3 2
−  1 5
-----
   1 7
```

# Unit 13: Mental Calculations

| Week | Learning Objectives | Thinking Skills | Resources |
|---|---|---|---|
| 7 | **(1) Mental addition**<br><br>Pupils will be able to:<br>• mentally add a 1-digit number to a 2-digit number less than 20<br>• mentally add a 2-digit number to tens<br>• mentally add using number bonds<br>• recognise tens and ones and add accordingly with number bonds | • Analysing parts and whole | • Pupil Textbook 1B, pp 63 to 64<br>• Practice Book 1C, pp 81 to 82<br>• Teacher's Guide 1B, pp 109 to 110 |
| 7 | **(2) Mental subtraction**<br><br>Pupils will be able to:<br>• mentally subtract a 1-digit number from another 1-digit number<br>• mentally subtract a 1-digit number from a 2-digit number with or without regrouping<br>• mentally subtract tens from a 2-digit number<br>• mentally subtract using number bonds or reverse addition<br>• apply the regrouping concept in subtraction<br><br>*Let's Explore!*<br><br>Pupils will be able to apply more than one strategy to add two 1-digit numbers by regrouping. | • Analysing parts and whole | • Pupil Textbook 1B, pp 65 to 69<br>• Practice Book 1C, pp 83 to 84<br>• Teacher's Guide 1B, pp 111 to 115 |

# Mental Calculations

**Learning objectives:**
**Mental addition**

**Pupils will be able to:**

- mentally add a 1-digit number to a 2-digit number less than 20
- mentally add a 2-digit number to tens
- mentally add using number bonds

- recognise tens and ones and add accordingly with number bonds

## Key concept

- A 2-digit number can be conceptualised as tens and ones
- Adding is conceptualised as adding or putting parts together

## Thinking skill

Analysing parts and whole

---

## Unit 13 Mental Calculations

Let's Learn!

**Mental addition**

① What is 12 + 6?

 Regroup 12 into tens and ones.

First add the ones.

$2 + 6 = 8$

Then add the result to the tens.

$10 + 8 = 18$

$12 + 6 = 18$

② What is 15 + 20?

 Regroup 15 into tens and ones.

First add the tens.

$10 + 20 = 30$

Then add the result to the ones.

$5 + 30 = 35$

$15 + 20 = 35$

③ **a** $13 + 4 = \boxed{17}$

 **b** $23 + 10 = \boxed{33}$

63

---

## Teaching sequence

- Explain the steps to mentally add 12 and 6:

 **Step 1**: Conceptualise 12 as 1 ten and 2 ones using number bonds.

 **Step 2**: Add the ones: 2 ones + 6 ones = 8 ones

 **Step 3**: Add the tens: 1 ten

 **Step 4**: Put the result together: 1 ten 8 ones → 18

- Explain the steps to mentally add 15 and 20:

 **Step 1**: Conceptualise 15 as 1 ten and 5 ones and 20 as 2 tens and 0 ones using number bonds.

 **Step 2**: Add the tens: 1 tens + 2 tens = 3 tens

 **Step 3**: Add the ones: 5 ones + 0 ones = 5 ones

 **Step 4**: Put the result together: 3 tens 5 ones → 35

- Look for pupils who can apply the strategy of adding numbers mentally without regrouping.

**What you will need**

- Set of cards numbered 4 to 9
- Set of cards numbered 6 to 9 (see Photocopy master 2 on page 284)

**Independent work**

Practice I in Practice Book IC, pp 81 to 82.

## Teaching sequence

**4** *Game*

- This game encourages pupils to practise addition of two I-digit numbers with regrouping.
- You may want to revise the 'making ten' strategy before asking pupils to play this game.

---

**Unit 13** Mental Calculations

**Game**

**4** **Add mentally!**

How to play:

Players: 2 to 4
You will need:
- a set of cards with numbers 4, 5, 6, 7, 8 and 9
- a set of cards with numbers 6, 7, 8 and 9

I   Player I takes a card from each set.

2   Player I adds the two numbers mentally.

8 + 5 = ?

3   The other players check the answer.

8 + 5 = 13    Correct!

4   You get I point for each correct answer.
Take turns to play.

The first player to get 5 points wins!

Practice Book IC, p.81

64

## Learning objectives: Mental subtraction

**Pupils will be able to:**

- mentally subtract a 1-digit number from another 1-digit number
- mentally subtract a 1-digit number from a 2-digit number with or without regrouping
- mentally subtract tens from a 2-digit number
- mentally subtract using number bonds or reverse addition
- apply the regrouping concept in subtraction

## Key concepts

- A 2-digit number can be conceptualised as tens and ones
- Subtracting is conceptualised as taking away from a whole

## Thinking skill

Analysing parts and whole

---

# Let's Learn!

## Mental subtraction

**1** What is 9 – 4?

Think of addition.
4 and 5 make 9.

9 – 4 = 5

**2** What is 8 – 5?

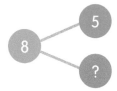

Think of addition.
5 and 3 make 8.

8 – 5 = 3

**3** What is 13 – 6?

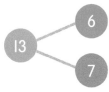

13 – 6 = 7

**4** What is 15 – 9?

15 – 9 = 6

## Teaching sequence

**1**

- Revise using number bonds in addition.
- Point out to pupils that to subtract is to find part of addition bond:
  9 – 4 = ?
  Think of the addition bond:
  4-5—9
  So 9 – 4 = 5.

**2**

- Look for pupils who can apply the strategy of mentally subtracting a 1-digit number from another 1-digit number.

**3** and **4**

- Note that these questions require pupils to subtract a 1-digit number from a 2-digit number. Explain and ask pupils to apply the strategy to work on these problems.
- Remind pupils how to use number bonds in addition involving 2-digit numbers.
- Point out to pupils that to subtract is to find the part of addition bond:
  13 – 6 = ?
  Think of the addition bond:
  6-7—13
  So 13 – 6 = 7.

Ask pupils to work in pairs.

Pupil A calls out a 2-digit number less than 40. Pupil B calls out a 1-digit number that is less than the ones digit given. Pupil A mentally subtracts the smaller number from the larger number.

Pupils A and B swap roles.

## Teaching sequence

- Point out to pupils that using addition bonds is not feasible when the numbers are large, like they are in this question.
- Show pupils the following strategy of regrouping the number 28 into tens and ones and then subtracting the corresponding tens and ones separately.

  **Step 1**: Recall number bonds and regroup the number into tens and ones:
  28—20-8

  **Step 2**: Subtract the tens:
  2 tens – 0 tens = 2 tens

  **Step 3**: Subtract the ones:
  8 ones – 3 ones = 5 ones

  **Step 4**: Put them together:
  2 tens 5 ones = 25

- Look for pupils who can apply the strategy described above.

---

**Unit 13** Mental Calculations

**5** What is 28 – 3?

Regroup 28 into tens and ones.

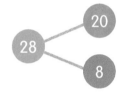

| First subtract the ones. | 8 – 3 = 5 |
| Then add the result to the tens. | 20 + 5 = 25 |

28 – 3 = 25

**6** What is 37 – 4?

Regroup 37 into tens and ones.

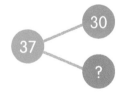

| First subtract the ones. | 7 – 4 = 3 |
| Then add the result to the tens. | 30 + 3 = 33 |

37 – 4 = 33

## Additional activity

Ask pupils to work in pairs.

Pupil A calls out a 2-digit number less than 40. Pupil B calls out a tens number. Pupil A mentally subtracts the smaller number from the larger number.

Pupils A and B swap roles.

**7** What is 39 – 10?

Regroup 39 into tens and ones.

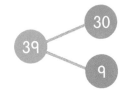

First subtract the tens.  $30 - 10 = 20$

Then add the result to the ones.  $9 + 20 = 29$

$39 - 10 = 29$

**8** What is 35 – 20?

Regroup 35 into tens and ones.

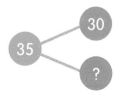

First subtract the tens.  $30 - \boxed{20} = \boxed{10}$

Then add the result to the ones.  $\boxed{5} + \boxed{10} = \boxed{15}$

$35 - 20 = \boxed{15}$

67

## Teaching sequence

**7**

- Explain the following strategy of regrouping the number 39 into tens and ones and then subtracting the corresponding tens and ones separately.

  **Step 1**: Recall number bonds and regroup the number into tens and ones:
  39—30-9

  **Step 2**: Subtract the tens:
  3 tens – 1 ten = 2 tens

  **Step 3**: Subtract the ones:
  9 ones – 0 ones = 9 ones

  **Step 4**: Put them together:
  2 tens 9 ones = 29

**8**

- Look for pupils who can apply the strategy described in **7**.
- Remind pupils to subtract the tens followed by the ones.

## What you will need

- Spinner with numbers 0 to 9
- Set of cards numbered from 11 to 19 (see Photocopy master 3 on pages 285 to 286)

## Additional activity

Ask pupils to work in pairs.

Pupils think of two 1-digit numbers. They discuss different ways to mentally subtract the two numbers.

## Independent work

Practice 2 in Practice Book IC, pp 83 to 84.

## Teaching sequence

**⑨** *Game*

- In this game, pupils are required to subtract a 1-digit number from a 2-digit number that is less than 20.
- The numbers may or may not require regrouping.
- Ask pupils to recall the addition bond.

  E.g.  15 − 6 = ?
  Recall the addition bond:
  15 = 9 + 6
  So 15 − 6 = 9.

---

## Game

**⑨ Subtract mentally!**

How to play:

**Players:** 2 to 4
**You will need:**
- a spinner with numbers 0 to 9
- a set of cards with numbers 11 to 19

**1** Player 1 takes a card from the set.

**2** Then they spin the spinner once to get another number.

**3** Next they subtract the smaller number from the greater number.

15 − 6 = ?

**4** The other players check the answer.
You get 1 point for each correct answer.
Take turns to play.

I win!

The first player to get 5 points wins!

68

Practice Book IC, p.83

---

## Objective of activity

Pupils will be able to apply more
than one strategy to add two
1-digit numbers by regrouping.

## Let's Explore!

⑩ There are many ways to add two 1-digit
numbers mentally.

### Example

8 + 7 = ?

This is one way:

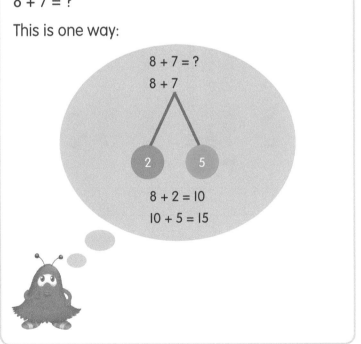

Think of another way to add 7 and 8 mentally.

Now think of two different ways to add 6 and 7.

Answers vary

69

## Teaching sequence

⑩ *Let's Explore!*

- In this activity, pupils are able
  to explore the different ways
  of adding two 1-digit numbers.

- These are some methods
  that pupils can use to add
  numbers mentally:

  (a) Recalling number bond:
      7—2-5
      8 + 2 + 5 = 10 + 5 = 15

  (b) Recalling another number
      bond:
      8—5-3
      5 + 3 + 7 = 5 + 10 = 15

  (c) The following is an
      unusual way:
      8—5-3
      7 = 2 + 5
      3 + 5 + 2 + 5 = 5 + 10 = 15

- Ask pupils to apply similar
  methods to find the sum of 6
  and 7.

# Unit 13    Mental Calculations

| Practice 1 | **Mental addition** |

1. Think of tens and ones.
   Add the numbers mentally.

┌─────────────────────┐
│  14 + 3 = ___17___  │
│     (10) (4)        │
└─────────────────────┘

a   15 + 2 = ___17___

b   35 + 1 = ___36___

c   23 + 5 = ___28___

d   22 + 7 = ___29___

e   30 + 9 = ___39___

f   32 + 6 = ___38___

g   34 + 5 = ___39___

2. Add the numbers mentally.
   First add the tens.
   Then add the tens and ones.

┌─────────────────────┐
│  13 + 10 = 23       │
│     (10) (3)        │
└─────────────────────┘

a   10 + 18 = ___28___

b   20 + 11 = ___31___

c   20 + 12 = ___32___

d   20 + 14 = ___34___

e   20 + 16 = ___36___

f   20 + 19 = ___39___

g   17 + 10 = ___27___

h   13 + 20 = ___33___

Date: _____

## Practice 2   Mental subtraction

**1** Think of addition.
Then subtract the numbers.

a   8 – 5 = _3_    b   9 – 6 = _3_

c   11 – 3 = _8_    d   13 – 7 = _6_

e   15 – 7 = _8_    f   12 – 8 = _4_

g   14 – 7 = _7_    h   11 – 9 = _2_

**2** Think of tens and ones.
Then subtract the numbers mentally.

a   28 – 4 = _24_    b   29 – 5 = _24_

c   27 – 6 = _21_    d   37 – 2 = _35_

e   38 – 8 = _30_    f   36 – 6 = _30_

**3** Subtract the numbers mentally.
First subtract the tens.
Then add the tens and ones.

a   22 – 10 = _12_    b   24 – 10 = _14_

c   23 – 20 = _3_    d   25 – 10 = _15_

e   31 – 10 = _21_    f   36 – 20 = _16_

g   33 – 10 = _23_    h   38 – 20 = _18_

i   35 – 30 = _5_    j   37 – 30 = _7_

---

**3** Solve these problems mentally.
Write your answers in the boxes.

a   Ella

> I have
> 30 stickers.
> I want 5 more.

How many stickers will Ella have
in the end?

`35`

b

> There are 18 marbles
> in the box.
> I put 20 more marbles
> into it.

How many marbles are there in the box
in the end?

`38`

c

> There are 10
> chocolate cakes
> and 19
> cheesecakes.

How many cakes are there altogether?

`29`

**4** Solve these problems mentally.
Write your answers in the boxes.

**a**

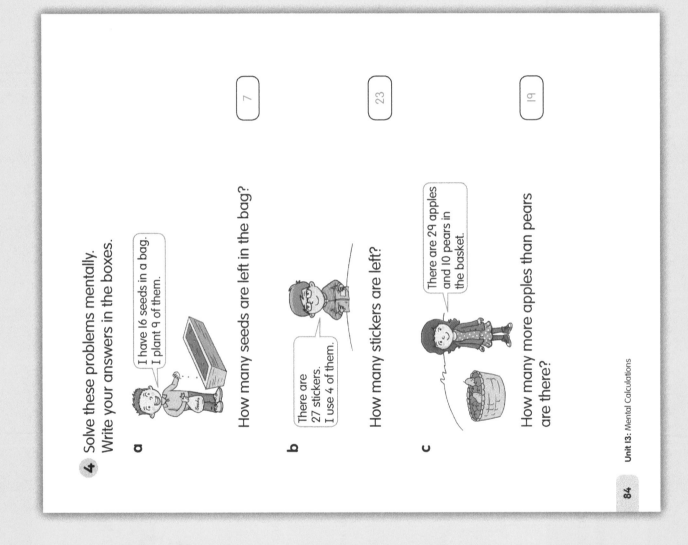

I have 16 seeds in a bag.
I plant 9 of them.

How many seeds are left in the bag?

7

**b**

There are
27 stickers.
I use 4 of them.

How many stickers are left?

23

**c**

There are 29 apples
and 10 pears in
the basket.

How many more apples than pears
are there?

19

Unit 13: Mental Calculations

84

| Week | Learning Objectives | Thinking Skills | Resources |
|---|---|---|---|
| 8 | **(1) Adding the same number**<br><br>Pupils will be able to:<br>• relate repeated addition to the multiplication concept<br>• use concrete representations to show the concept of multiplication as repeated addition<br>• conceptualise multiplication as groups of items | • Applying the addition concept to the multiplication concept | • Pupil Textbook 1B, pp 70 to 72<br>• Practice Book 1C, pp 85 to 90<br>• Teacher's Guide 1B, pp 122 to 124 |
| 8 | **(2) Making up multiplication stories**<br><br>Pupils will be able to:<br>• write repeated addition as multiplication statements<br>• write the multiplication statement from a situation given the number of groups and items in each group<br>• interpret multiplication sentences: the first factor referring to the number of groups and the second factor as the number of items in each group<br>• relate multiplication stories and write multiplication statements | • Relating and applying the multiplication concept to given situations | • Pupil Textbook 1B, pp 73 to 75<br>• Practice Book 1C, pp 91 to 94<br>• Teacher's Guide 1B, pp 125 to 127 |

| Week | Learning Objectives | Thinking Skills | Resources |
|------|--------------------|----------------|-----------|
| | *Maths Journal*<br><br>Pupils will be able to:<br>• pick out the correct statements and explain why the others are incorrect<br>• make multiplication sentences | | |
| 9 | **(3) Solving word problems**<br><br>Pupils will be able to:<br>• use picture representation to solve word problems on multiplication<br>• use the multiplication concept (group and items) to solve problems<br>• write multiplication statements for word problems<br><br>*Let's Explore!*<br><br>Pupils will be able to:<br>• arrange objects in different ways (rows and columns)<br>• make multiplication sentences | • Applying the multiplication concept | • Pupil Textbook IB, pp 76 to 78<br>• Practice Book IC, pp 95 to 98<br>• Teacher's Guide IB, pp 128 to 130 |

# Unit 14: Multiplication

Medium-term plan

| Week | Learning Objectives | Thinking Skills | Resources |
|---|---|---|---|
| 9 | *Put On Your Thinking Caps!* | • Applying the multiplication concept<br><br>Heuristics for problem solving:<br>• Act it out<br>• Draw a model | • Pupil Textbook 1B p 78<br>• Practice Book 1C, pp 99 to 100<br>• Teacher's Guide 1B, p 130 |
| | Review 5 | | • Practice Book 1C, pp 101 to 104 |

## Summative assessment opportunities

Assessment Book 1, Test 6, pp 69 to 74
For extension, Assessment Book 1, Challenging Problems 3, pp 75 to 76
Assessment Book 1, Check-up 3, pp 76 to 90

# Multiplication

## Learning objectives: Adding the same number

**Pupils will be able to:**

- relate repeated addition to the multiplication concept
- use concrete representations to show the concept of multiplication as repeated addition
- conceptualise multiplication as groups of items

## Teaching sequence

- Show 3 bowls with 2 cubes in each bowl. Ask pupils questions to help them describe what they see:

  *"How many bowls are there?"*

  *"How many cubes are there in each bowl?"*

  *"How many cubes are there altogether?"*

- Show how this can be represented using the following to show the total number of cubes:
  - 2 + 2 + 2 = 6
  - 3 twos = 6
  - 3 groups of 2

## Key concept

Multiplication is conceptualised as repeated addition.

## What you will need

- 6 counters, e.g., cubes
- 3 containers, e.g., plastic bowls

---

### Unit 14 Multiplication

Let's Learn!

**Adding the same number**

How many groups of toys are there?

How many toys are there in each group?

2 toys          2 toys          2 toys

There are 3 groups.

Each group has 2 toys.

2 + 2 + 2 = 6

   3 twos = 6

3 groups of 2 = 6

There are 6 toys altogether.

2 + 2 + 2 means 3 twos or 3 groups of 2

70

---

## Thinking skills

Applying the addition concept to multiplication

## Additional activity

Ask pupils to work in pairs.

Pupil A calls out a multiplication statement, e.g. 2 groups of 5 or two fives. Pupil B arranges 2 groups of 5 beads or any other counters to reflect the statement. Pupil A checks whether the representation is correct.

Pupils A and B swap roles.

## Teaching sequence

**2**

- Look for pupils who can use repeated addition to help them complete the multiplication statement.
- Point out to pupils that there are 3 different ways to represent the situation:
  - Repeated addition: $5 + 5 + 5 + 5 = 20$
  - Multiplication statement: 4 fives = 20
  - Another way of writing a multiplication statement: 4 groups of 5

**3**

- Ask pupils to use repeated addition to complete the multiplication statement.

---

**2**

There are [ 4 ] groups.

Each group has [ 5 ] marbles.

[ 5 ] + [ 5 ] + [ 5 ] + [ 5 ] = [ 20 ]

[ 4 ] fives = [ 20 ]

[ 4 ] groups of 5 = [ 20 ]

There are [ 20 ] marbles altogether.

**3**

[ 4 ] + [ 4 ] + [ 4 ] = [ 12 ]

[ 3 ] fours = [ 12 ]

[ 3 ] groups of 4 = [ 12 ]

There are [ 12 ] stars altogether.

71

## Teaching sequence

- The objective of this section is for pupils to complete an activity designed to reflect their understanding of multiplication concepts.

- For **a**, show pupils how to put the correct number of counters onto each plate. Write the repeated addition statement, grouping statement and the total number of counters on the board.

- Ask pupils to work in groups to complete the exercises in the textbook and share their answers with the class.

- For **c**, point out to pupils that they can put any equal number of counters on the 3 plates. Complete the repeated addition statement and multiplication statement.

## What you will need
- 28 counters for each group
- 7 containers for each group

## Additional activity

Ask pupils to make as many different groups using the counters as they can, e.g., 3 ones, 3 twos, 3 threes, 3 fours, etc. Through this, pupils will also incidentally learn the 3 times table.

## Independent work

Practice I in Practice Book IC, pp 85 to 90.

---

Unit 14 Multiplication

## Activity

4 How many counters are there?

**a** Take 5 plates.
Put 2 counters on each plate.

| 2 | + | 2 | + | 2 | + | 2 | + | 2 | = | 10 |

5 twos = 10

5 groups of 2 = 10

**b** Take 6 plates.
Put 3 counters on each plate.

| 3 | + | 3 | + | 3 | + | 3 | + | 3 | + | 3 |

= 18

6 threes = 18

6 groups of 3 = 18

**c** Take 3 plates.
Put an equal number of counters on each plate.

☐ + ☐ + ☐ = ☐     Answers vary

3 ☐ = ☐

3 groups of ☐ = ☐

Practice Book IC, p.85

72

---

## Learning objectives: Making up multiplication stories

**Pupils will be able to:**

- write repeated addition as multiplication statements
- write the multiplication statement from a situation given the number of groups and items in each group
- interpret multiplication sentences: the first factor referring to the number of groups and the second factor as the number of items in each group
- relate multiplication stories and write multiplication statements

## Key concept

Tell stories based on the multiplication concept and repeated addition.

## Thinking skill

Relating and applying the multiplication concept to given situations

## What you will need

5 pairs of shoes or socks

---

Multiplication **Unit 14**

# Let's Learn!

## Making up multiplication stories

Ella has 5 groups of socks.
Each group has 2 socks.

$2 + 2 + 2 + 2 + 2 = 10$

5 groups of $2 = 10$

$5 \times 2 = 10$

There are 10 socks.

> × is read as **times**.
> It stands for **multiplication**.
> It means to put all the groups together.

$5 \times 2 = 10$ is a **multiplication sentence**.
It says **five times two equals ten**.

Tai puts his toys into 5 groups in this way.

He is trying to write a multiplication sentence.

 Can he do it?

73

## Teaching sequence

- Show the picture of 5 pairs of socks. Tell the multiplication story in the different ways:
  - $2 + 2 + 2 + 2 + 2 = 10$
  - 5 twos = 10
  - 5 groups of 2
- Next introduce another way of showing the set of 5 pairs of socks:

  $5 \times 2 = 10$

- Emphasise that there should be equal number of items in each set.
- Explain why the second example is incorrect. Encourage pupils to explain why it is not possible to write $5 \times 2$ in the example.

## Teaching sequence

- Ask pupils to attempt this question and gauge their ability to phrase the multiplication story.

- Ask pupils to work in pairs to make up multiplication stories and write addition and multiplication statements on the situations given.
- Encourage groups to share their answers with the class.

---

**Unit 14** Multiplication

**2** Tell a multiplication story about these fish.

I see 〔 4 〕 groups of fish.

Each group has 〔 3 〕 fish.

〔 4 〕 × 〔 3 〕 = 〔 12 〕

There are 〔 12 〕 fish.

---

**Activity**

**3** Tell multiplication stories about these things.
Write the multiplication sentences.

a
$3 \times 2 = 6$

b
$8 \times 2 = 16$

c
$6 \times 4 = 24$

Practice Book IC, p.91

74

## Objectives of activity

Pupils will be able to:

- pick out the correct statements and explain why the others are incorrect
- make multiplication sentences

### Maths Journal

**4** Read the sentences.
Which are correct?

**a** $4 \times 5 = 20$ ✓

**b** $5 \times 2$ has the answer 52.

**c** The pictures show $4 \times 4$.

**d** $8 \times 3 = 3 + 3 + 3 + 3 + 3 + 3 + 3 + 3$ ✓

**e** $2 \times 6 = 6 + 6 + 6 + 6 + 6 + 6$

**f** $4 \times 7 = 7 + 7 + 7 + 7 = 28$ ✓

Think of some numbers.
Make multiplication sentences using these numbers.

Answers vary

75

## Teaching sequence

**4** *Maths Journal*

**a**

- Use this question to assess pupils' understanding of multiplication.
- Take note of pupils' common misconceptions by the incorrect answers they select.

**b**

- Encourage pupils to write a multiplication statement and find the answer.
- Use this question to assess whether pupils have understood the 'repeated addition' concept for multiplication.

## Learning objectives: Solving word problems

**Pupils will be able to:**

- use picture representation to solve word problems on multiplication
- use the multiplication concept (group and items) to solve problems
- write multiplication statements for word problems

## Key concept

Applying the multiplication concept to solve word problems.

## Thinking skill

Applying the multiplication concept

## What you will need

40 counters or buttons

## Teaching sequence

- Read the question together. Explain and relate the problem to the multiplication concept.
- Write out the multiplication statement. Explain and relate it to the problem.

  *3 × 6 = 18*

- At this stage, pupils are not expected to have mastered the times tables. Instead, pupils will need to use repeated addition to find the answer.
- Discourage them from using the 'counting' method.

- Ask pupils to work in pairs to read and discuss the question.
- Then ask them to write a multiplication statement to find the answer.

---

Unit 14 Multiplication

### Let's Learn!

**Solving word problems**

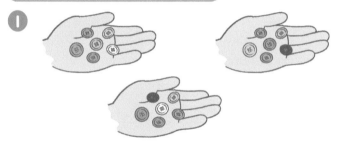

There are 3 children.

A teacher gives each child 6 buttons.

How many buttons does the teacher give out altogether?

3 × 6 = 18

The teacher gives out 18 buttons altogether.

Farha has 2 baskets.

There are 4 carrots in each basket.

How many carrots does Farha have altogether?

2 × 4 = 8

Farha has 8 carrots altogether.

76

## Independent work

Practice 3 and *Maths Journal* in
Practice Book IC, pp 95 to 98.

Peter has 5 plates.

He puts 4 cherries on
each plate.

5 × 4 = 20
20 cherries

How many cherries does Peter have altogether?

The plant has 6 leaves.

Ruby sees 4 ladybirds on
every leaf.

6 × 4 = 24
24 ladybirds

How many ladybirds does Ruby see altogether?

Practice Book IC, p.95

77

## Teaching sequence

3 and 4

• Ask pupils to work individually.
• Invite volunteers to write the
  multiplication statements and
  find the answers.

## Objectives of activity

Pupils will be able to:

- arrange objects in different ways (rows and columns)
- make multiplication sentences

## Thinking skill

Applying the multiplication concept

## Heuristics for problem solving

- Act it out
- Draw a model

## Teaching sequence

**⑤** *Let's Explore!*

- Ask pupils to work in pairs or groups.

**a**

- Ask pupils to look at the pictures in the textbook. Link the diagram of 12 balls to the multiplication statement: *3 × 4 = 12*
- Emphasise the words 'rows' and 'columns'.
- Then ask pupils to rearrange the balls in different ways, emphasising that there must be the same number of balls in each row.

**b**

- Ask pupils to repeat the same activity using 18 balls.

**⑥** *Put On Your Thinking Caps!*

- Ask pupils to read the question out loud and choose the correct statement.
- Encourage pupils to draw stick figures or models to find the answer.
- Ask pupils to explain why the other options are incorrect.

## What you will need

18 counters or balls

## Additional activity

Ask pupils to work in pairs. Encourage them to make up stories involving the multiplication concept.

## Independent work

*Challenging Practice, Problem Solving* and Review 5 in Practice Book IC, pp 99 to 104.

---

Unit 14  Multiplication

### Let's Explore!

**⑤** **a** You have 12 balls.
Arrange them into rows in different ways.
Each row must have the same number of balls.
Write a multiplication sentence for each arrangement.

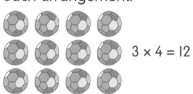

3 × 4 = 12

**b** You have 18 balls.
Do the same as above.
How many multiplication sentences can you write?

### Put On Your Thinking Caps!

**⑥** Omar has 3 rabbits.
Which one of the following shows the number of legs Omar's rabbits have altogether?

3 + 3 + 3 = 9          3 + 3 = 6

3 × 4 = 12          3 × 3 = 9

A rabbit has 4 legs.
There are 3 rabbits.
3 × 4 = 12

Practice Book IC, p.99    Practice Book IC, p.100

78

# Unit 14 Multiplication

Date: _____

## Practice 1   Adding the same number

1   First count the number of groups of bugs.
    Then count the number of bugs in each group.
    Write the answers in the spaces.

They are in 2 groups

There are 3 bugs in each group.

$3 + 3 = \underline{6}$ .............. 2 threes = $\underline{6}$

a

$2 + 2 + 2 + 2 = \underline{10}$ .......... 5 twos = $\underline{10}$

**2** Look at the pictures.
Fill in the boxes.

**a**

$2 + 2 + 2 + 2 + 2 + 2 = 12$

$2 + 2 = 12$

6 twos = 12

There are 12 snails altogether.

**b**

$4 + 4 + 4 + 4 = 16$

$4 + 4 = 16$

4 fours = 16

There are 16 ladybirds altogether.

---

**b**

$5 + 5 + 5 + 5 = \underline{20}$ . . . . . . . . . . 4 fives = $\underline{20}$

**c**

$4 + 4 + 4 = \underline{12}$ . . . . . . . . . . 3 fours = $\underline{12}$

**d**

 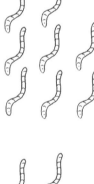 

$8 + 8 = \underline{16}$ . . . . . . . . . . 2 eights = $\underline{16}$

4 Look at the legs in the pictures.
Then fill in the spaces.

a A child has ___2___ legs.

2 + 2 + 2 + 2 = ___8___

4 twos = ___8___

4 children have ___8___ legs.

b A spider has ___8___ legs.

8 + 8 + 8 = ___24___

3 eights = ___24___

3 spiders have ___24___ legs.

c An ant has ___6___ legs.

6 + 6 + 6 + 6 + 6 + 6 = ___36___

6 sixes = ___36___

6 ants have ___36___ legs.

3 Look at the pictures.
Fill in the spaces.

**Example**

There are ___10___ rabbits. 2 **fives** = ___10___

a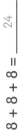

There are ___8___ frogs. 4 ___twos___ = ___8___

b

There are ___25___ fish. 5 ___fives___ = ___25___

**Date:** _____

## Practice 2   Making up multiplication stories

**1** Complete the number sentences.

**Example**

6 + 6 = __12__

2 × 6 = __12__

**a** 4 + 4 + 4 = __12__

3 × __4__ = __12__

**b** 3 + 3 + 3 = __9__

__3__ × 3 = __9__

**c** 2 + 2 + 2 + 2 = __8__

4 × __2__ = __8__

**2** Complete the addition and multiplication sentences.
Then fill in the spaces.

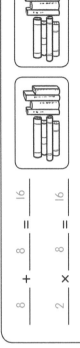

8 + __8__ = __16__

2 × __8__ = __16__

Millie has __2__ groups of books.

Each group has __8__ books.

There are __16__ books altogether.

---

**5** Look at these pictures.
Then fill in the spaces.

**a** A starfish has __5__ arms.

6 __fives__ = __30__

6 starfishes have __30__ arms.

**b** An octopus has __8__ tentacles.

4 __eights__ = __32__

4 octopuses have __32__ tentacles.

**c** One flower has __6__ petals.

6 __sixes__ = __36__

6 flowers have __36__ petals.

**3** a

$5 + 5 + 5 = 15$

$3 \times 5 = 15$

Omar has ___3___ groups of balloons.

Each group has ___5___ balloons.

There are ___15___ balloons altogether.

b $6 + 6 + 6 + 6 =$ [ 24 ]

[ 4 ] × [ 6 ] = [ 24 ]

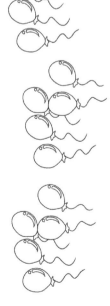

Ruby has ___4___ groups of marbles.

Each group has ___6___ marbles.

There are ___24___ marbles altogether.

c [ 3 ] ( + ) [ 3 ] ( + ) [ 3 ] ( = ) [ 9 ]

[ 3 ] ( × ) [ 3 ] ( = ) [ 9 ]

Miya has ___3___ groups of strawberries.

Each group has ___3___ strawberries.

There are ___9___ strawberries altogether.

**4** Fill in the spaces.

a

How many jars are there ? ___2___

How many fish are in each jar? ___6___

How many fish are there altogether?

$2 \times 6 = 12$

There are ___12___ fish altogether.

Date: _____

## Practice 3  Solving word problems

1 Solve these word problems.

a There are 2 plates.
Each plate has 5 strawberries.
How many strawberries are there?

$5 + 5 = \underline{10}$

$2 \times 5 = \underline{10}$

There are ___10___ strawberries.

b There are 6 bags.
Each bag has 3 pockets.
How many pockets are there?

$\boxed{3} + \boxed{3} + \boxed{3} + \boxed{3} + \boxed{3} + \boxed{3} = \boxed{18}$

$\boxed{6} \times \boxed{3} = \boxed{18}$

There are ___18___ pockets.

b

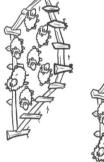

pen

How many pens are there ? ___3___

How many sheep are in each pen? ___7___

How many sheep are there altogether?

___3___ × ___7___ = ___21___

There are ___21___ sheep altogether.

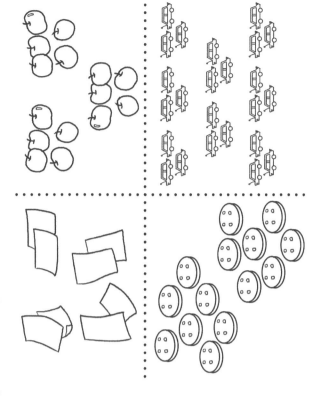

**c** Tim has 4 jars.
There are 6 marbles in each jar.
How many marbles does Tim have altogether?

[ 4 ] [ × ] [ 6 ] [ = ] [ 24 ]

Tim has __24__ marbles altogether.

**d** Kerry has 5 boxes.
There are 8 pencils in each box.

[ 5 ] [ × ] [ 8 ] [ = ] [ 40 ]

Kerry has __40__ pencils altogether.

---

Date: _____

## Maths Journal

**1** Look at the pictures below.

Which of these are shown in the pictures?
Circle them.

2 × 8    (4 × 2)    (8 × 3)    9 × 3    2 × 2

(3 × 5)    7 × 3    4 × 8    (2 × 7)    6 × 3

Date: _____

## Challenging Practice

1 Fill in the missing numbers.

a

$6 + 6 + 6 + 6 + 6 =$ _____ 5 groups of 6

b

$2 + 2 + 2 + 2 =$ _____ 4 groups of 2

c

$5 + 5 + 5 + 5$

= _____ 4 groups of 5

d

$8 + 8 + 8 + 8 + 8$

= 5 groups of _____ 8

---

2 Look at the pictures.
Write a multiplication story for each picture.

**Example**

There are 2 groups of biscuits.

Each group has 2 biscuits.

2 groups of 2 = 4

2 × 2 = 4

There are 4 biscuits altogether.

There are 4 groups of marbles.

Each group has 5 marbles.

4 groups of 5 = 20

4 × 5 = 20

There are 20 marbles altogether.

marbles

# Review 5

**1** Add the numbers mentally.

**a** $12 + 5 =$ ___ 17    **b** $24 + 3 =$ ___ 27

**c** $21 + 8 =$ ___ 29    **d** $32 + 4 =$ ___ 36

**e** $10 + 23 =$ ___ 33    **f** $18 + 10 =$ ___ 28

**g** $20 + 17 =$ ___ 37    **h** $18 + 20 =$ ___ 38

**2** Subtract the numbers mentally.

**a** $11 - 5 =$ ___ 6    **b** $18 - 9 =$ ___ 9

**c** $23 - 2 =$ ___ 21    **d** $27 - 2 =$ ___ 25

**e** $26 - 10 =$ ___ 16    **f** $35 - 10 =$ ___ 25

**g** $30 - 20 =$ ___ 10    **h** $27 - 20 =$ ___ 7

---

## Problem Solving

**1** Hardeep has 6 tomatoes on one plate.
Miya has the same number of tomatoes as Hardeep on each plate.
How many tomatoes does Miya have altogether?

Hardeep          Miya

Miya has 18 tomatoes altogether.

**5** Fill in the spaces.

a  8 + 8 = _16_
   2 × 8 = _16_

b  3 + 3 + 3 + 3 + 3 = _15_
   5 × 3 = _15_

c  6 + 6 + 6 = _18_
   3 × 6 = _18_

d  9 + 9 + 9 + 9 = _36_
   4 × 9 = _36_

**6** Fill in the spaces.

a  2 fours = _8_

b  3 threes = _9_

c  4 fives = _20_

d  5 sixes = _30_

**7** There are 3 pages of stickers.
Each page has 6 stickers.
How many stickers are there altogether?

3 × 6 = 18

There are _18_ stickers altogether.

**3** Fill in the boxes.

5 + 5 + 5 + 5 = 20

4 fives = 20

**4** Fill in the spaces.

There are _6_ bowls.
Each bowl has _3_ fish.
There are _18_ fish altogether.

**8** There are 4 bags of apples.
Each bag has 6 apples.
How many apples are there altogether?

$4 \times 6 = 24$

There are ____24____ apples altogether.

**9** Peter gave all his marbles to Jack and Millie.
Each of them got 3 marbles.
How many marbles did Peter have at first?

Jack                    Millie

$2 \times 3 = 6$

Peter had ____6____ marbles.

# Unit 15: Division

| Week | Learning Objectives | Thinking Skills | Resources |
|---|---|---|---|
| 1 | **(1) Sharing equally**<br><br>Pupils will be able to:<br>• use concrete representations to show the concept of division as sharing equally<br>• use the strategy of distributing objects equally into groups | • Analysing parts and whole<br>• Comparing (objects) | • Pupil Textbook 1B, pp 79 to 80<br>• Practice Book 1D, pp 5 to 12<br>• Teacher's Guide 1B, pp 143 to 144 |
| 1 | **(2) Finding the number of groups**<br><br>Pupils will be able to:<br>• use concrete representations to show the concept of division as finding the number of groups<br>• use the strategy of distributing objects equally in each group | • Analysing parts and whole<br>• Comparing (objects) | • Pupil Textbook 1B, pp 81 to 83<br>• Practice Book 1D, pp 13 to 18<br>• Teacher's Guide 1B, pp 145 to 147 |
| 1 | *Let's Explore!*<br><br>Pupils will be able to use the concept of division to find the number of ways of dividing items into groups.<br><br>*Put On Your Thinking Caps!* | • Analysing parts and whole<br>• Comparing (numbers) | • Pupil Textbook 1B, p 83<br>• Practice Book 1D, pp 19 to 20<br>• Teacher's Guide 1B, p 147 |

# Division

**Learning objectives: Sharing equally**

**Pupils will be able to:**

- use concrete representations to show the concept of division as sharing equally
- use the strategy of distributing objects equally into groups

**Key concept**

Division is conceptualised as dividing a set of objects equally.

**Thinking skills**

- Analysing parts and whole
- Comparing (objects)

**What you will need**

- 20 oranges or counters
- Containers or paper plates

---

## Unit 15 Division

**Let's Learn!**

**Sharing equally**

❶ There are 12 oranges.
Tai has 4 friends.
He gives each friend the same number of oranges in a bag.

| Jack | Millie | Ella | Omar |
|------|--------|------|------|

Try putting 2 oranges in each bag. There are 4 oranges left.

Each friend gets 3 oranges.

Now put 1 more orange in each bag. There are no oranges left.

79

---

**Teaching sequence**

❶

- Explain the meaning of sharing and sharing equally. Highlight that in sharing, we need to have a set of items to be shared and the number of people who receive the set of items.

- Relate this definition to the example given in the textbook. There are 12 oranges to be shared and 4 people to receive the set of items.

- Next explain the strategy of sharing the number of items.

  **Step 1**: Think of a number that each person should get. In the example, we think of 2 oranges for each person, but there are 4 oranges left.

  **Step 2**: Then distribute the rest equally to each person. In this case each person gets one more orange.

- Show an example that is not possible. For example, you can show that trying to give each person 4 oranges would not be possible as there are not enough oranges to be shared.

## Additional activity

- Give pupils other scenarios and ask them to share equally.

  E.g. *Mrs Green has 3 children. She has 9 toys. How many toys does each child get?*

  Draw 3 circles on the board. Then ask pupils to draw the number of toys shared equally on the board.

- Encourage pupils to practise this with similar questions to the example above.

## What you will need

- 20 counters for each group
- 4 plates for each group

## Independent work

Practice I in Practice Book ID, pp 5 to 12.

## Teaching sequence

- Ask pupils to work in pairs. Give each pair 4 plates and 20 counters and ask them to apply the strategy given earlier to place the counters equally on each plate.
- Ask them to think of different numbers that can be placed on each plate and try out each case.
- Encourage pupils to use the following sentences:

  *"There are 20 counters to be divided equally between 4 plates (groups)."*

  *"There are 5 counters on each plate."*

- Assess pupils' understanding of the concept by asking them to answer the questions.
- Ask pupils to copy and complete the sentences in the textbook.

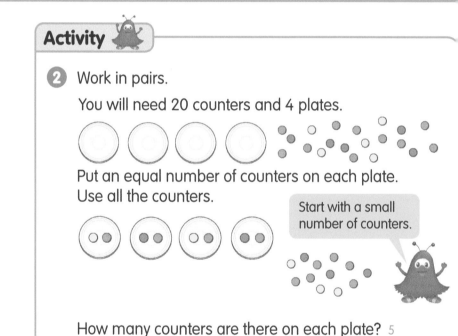

Unit I5  Division

### Activity

**2** Work in pairs.

You will need 20 counters and 4 plates.

Put an equal number of counters on each plate. Use all the counters.

> Start with a small number of counters.

How many counters are there on each plate? 5

**3**

How many cherries are there altogether?  I5

How many cakes are there?  3

Put the same number of cherries on each cake.

Each cake has  5  cherries.

Practice Book ID, p.5

80

## Learning objectives: Finding the number of groups

**Pupils will be able to:**

- use concrete representations to show the concept of division as finding the number of groups
- use the strategy of distributing objects equally in each group

## Key concept

Division is conceptualised as sharing a set of items equally into groups.

## Thinking skills

- Analysing parts and whole
- Comparing (objects)

## What you will need

- 12 eggs
- 3 bowls
- 20 counters, e.g., cubes
- Containers, e.g., paper plates

---

## Let's Learn!

### Finding the number of groups

**1** There are 12 eggs.
Put 4 eggs into each bowl.
How many bowls do you need?

First put 4 eggs into 1 bowl.

Do this until all the eggs are put into the bowls.

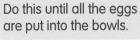

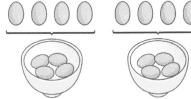 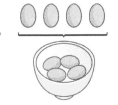

You need 3 bowls.

**2** Millie has 15 toy cars.
She puts 3 toy cars on each mat.
How many mats does she need for all the toy cars?

She needs [ 5 ] mats for all the toy cars.

81

## Teaching sequence

 **1**

- Encourage pupils to compare this with the previous question and explain the difference between the two sets of questions.

- Point out to pupils that:
  - the purpose of the previous question is to find the number of items in each group.
  - the purpose of this question is to find the number of groups.

- Using the eggs and bowls, demonstrate the strategy to find the number of groups:

  **Step 1**: Take out 4 eggs and place them together as a group in a bowl.

  **Step 2**: Continue to take out 4 eggs and place them in groups until all the eggs have been grouped into the bowls.

  **Step 3**: Then count the number of groups or bowls used.

**2**

- Use the question to assess pupils' understanding of finding the number of groups. Ask pupils to work in pairs and apply the strategy to solve the problem.

- Give pupils plates and counters for support.

What you will need
- 12 marbles and paper cups for each group
- 20 marbles and paper cups for each group

Independent work
Practice 2 in Practice Book ID, pp 13 to 18.

## Teaching sequence

**a**
- Ask pupils to work in groups. Give each group 12 marbles and some cups.
- Explain to pupils that they have divided the marbles into groups of 3 and then 4. Ask them to find out how many groups there are in each case.
- Encourage pupils to think of other numbers of items that make equal groups (2, 6 or 1 in each group).

**b**
- Give each group 20 marbles. Ask pupils to find out how many cups are needed when different numbers of marbles are put in each cup.
- Encourage volunteers to show how they find the number of cups needed. E.g. If they place 2 marbles in each cup, they would need 10 cups.
- Ask groups to show their answers by drawing circles representing the number of groups (cups) and drawing counters inside the circles to show the number of items in each group. Then ask them to write the division statements: *There are 2 marbles in each cup. 10 cups are used.*
- Finally, ask groups to present their solutions to the class.

---

**Unit 15** Division

### Activity

**3** **a** You will need 12 marbles and some cups.

> Put 3 marbles in each cup.
> How many cups do you need? 4 cups

> Put 4 marbles in each cup.
> How many cups do you need? 3 cups

**b** You will need 20 marbles and some cups.

> Put 2 marbles in each cup.
> How many cups do you need? 10 cups

> Put 4 marbles in each cup.
> How many cups do you need? 5 cups

> Put 5 marbles in each cup.
> How many cups do you need? 4 cups

> Put 10 marbles in each cup.
> How many cups do you need? 2 cups

Practice Book ID, p.13

82

## Objective of activity

Pupils will be able to use the concept of division to find the number of ways of dividing items into groups.

## Thinking skills

- Analysing parts and whole
- Comparing (numbers)

## Heuristics for problem solving

- Act it out
- Draw a model

## What you will need

- 24 cubes for each group
- Paper plates for each group

## Independent work

*Challenging Practice* and *Problem Solving* in Practice Book ID, pp 19 to 20.

---

Division **Unit 15**

### Let's Explore!

4 Work in pairs.
You will need 24 .
Use all the  and divide them into groups.
Each group must have the same number of .
How many ways can you do it?

### Maths Journal

5 Draw the different ways you can group the  in your journal.

### Put On Your Thinking Caps!

6 Chris has 18 marbles.
He puts them into groups.
Each group has 5 marbles.

Draw pictures to help you or act it out.

**a** What is the greatest number of groups Chris can have? 3 groups

**b** How many marbles are not used? 3 marbles

Practice Book ID, p.19    Practice Book ID, p.20

83

## Teaching sequence

4 *Let's Explore!*

- Ask pupils to explore the different numbers of groups they can make with all the cubes.
- Remind pupils that each group must have an equal number of cubes.
- Ask groups to present their answers.

5 *Maths Journal*

- Encourage pupils to draw the different ways that they grouped the cubes.

6 *Put On Your Thinking Caps!*

- Note that in this question, there would be a remainder after dividing the items equally.
- Ask pupils to read the question, then use items they have to distribute 5 'marbles' for each group and find out the number of groups they can get if they have 18 'marbles'.
- Pupils will find that they have a remainder of 3 'marbles'. Ask them to draw pictures to solve the problem and to explain their answers.

# INSPIRE MATHS

# PRACTICE BOOK 1D

Noogal    Toogal    Zoogal    Googol    Ooogol    Koogol

Consultant and author
Dr Fong Ho Kheong

**Authors**
Chelvi Ramakrishnan and Bernice Lau Pui Wah

**UK consultants**
Carole Skinner, Simon d'Angelo and Elizabeth Gibbs

---

Date: _____

## Unit 15  Division

Practice 1    **Sharing equally**

1  Look at the bags of oranges.
   Then fill in the spaces.

a

There are ___6___ oranges altogether.
How many oranges are there in each
bag? ___2___

b

There are ___12___ oranges altogether.
How many oranges are there in each
bag? ___4___

**c**

There are __4__ badgers altogether.

There are __4__ holes.

There is __1__ badger in each hole.

**d**

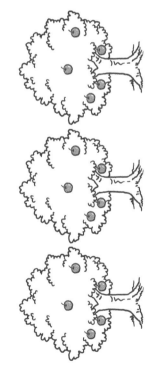

There are __12__ cats altogether.

There are __3__ baskets.

There are __4__ cats in each basket.

---

② Look at the pictures.
Then fill in the spaces.

**a**

There are __4__ fish altogether.

There are __2__ bowls.

There are __2__ fish in each bowl.

**b**

There are __15__ apples altogether.

There are __3__ trees.

There are __5__ apples on each tree.

**b** Peter is in the garden.
He has to put 10 flowers into 2 equal groups.

Peter has put 1 flower in each group.
Help Peter to complete the flowers in each group.

 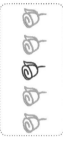

Each group has ___5___ flowers.

**c** Ruby is in the library.
She needs to put 15 books into 5 equal groups.

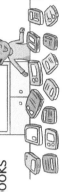 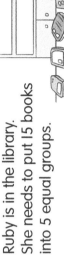

Ruby puts 2 books in each group.
Help Ruby to continue.

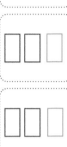

Each group has ___3___ books.

**3 a** Jack is tidying the shoe rack.
He has to put 8 shoes into 4 equal groups.

He puts 1 shoe in each group.

Then he puts 1 more in each group.

Each group has ___2___ shoes.

**5** **a** There are 15 toys.
Peter packs them into 5 boxes equally.
How many toys are there in each box?

There are ___3___ toys in each box.

**b** There are 6 balls.
They are shared equally by 3 children.
How many balls does each child get?

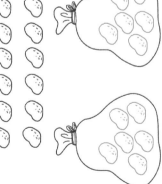

Each child gets ___2___ balls.

**4** **a** There are 12 potatoes.
Draw an equal number of potatoes in each bag.

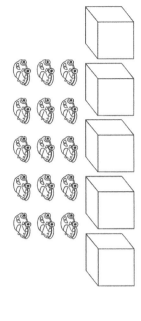

There are ___6___ potatoes in each bag.

**b** There are 16 marbles.
Draw an equal number of marbles for each child.

Each child gets ___4___ marbles.

## Practice 2  Finding the number of groups

**1 a** There are 10 children.
Circle groups of 5.

There are ___2___ groups of 5.

**b** There are 16 fish.
Circle groups of 4.

There are ___4___ groups of 4.

---

**6 a** Divide 18 coins into 3 equal groups.

There are ___6___ coins in each group.

**b** Divide 20 pencils into 5 equal groups.

There are ___4___ pencils in each group.

**c** There are 15 oranges.
Circle groups of 3.

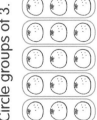

There are _____5_____ groups of 3.

**d** 12 children go skating.
Circle the children in groups of 4.

There are _____3_____ groups of 4 children.

**e** There are 18 carrots.
Circle the carrots in groups of 3.

There are _____6_____ groups of 3 carrots.

**f** Jack makes 20 sandwiches.
Circle the sandwiches in groups of 4.

There are _____5_____ groups of 4 sandwiches.

**2** Read the story.
Then fill in the spaces.

**a** There are 10 gloves.
Mrs Brook gives 2 gloves to each child.
How many children are there?

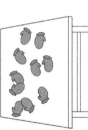

There are __5__ children.

**b** There are 12 coins.
Farha puts 4 coins into each money box.
How many money boxes are there?

There are __3__ money boxes.

**c** Some squirrels eat 20 nuts altogether.
Each squirrel eats 2 nuts.
How many squirrels are there?

There are __10__ squirrels.

**3** Read the story.
Then fill in the spaces.

**a** Omar collects stickers.
He has 20 stickers.
He puts 5 stickers on each page of his album.
How many pages does he need?

He needs __4__ pages.

**b** Mr Lee buys 8 plums to make plum pies.
He uses 4 plums to make each plum pie.
How many plum pies does he make?

He makes __2__ plum pies.

**c** Ruby buys 15 oranges.
She divides them equally into boxes.
Each box has 5 oranges.
How many boxes does she use?

She uses __3__ boxes.

## Challenging Practice

1 Miya collects rubbers.
Look at her rubbers.
Then fill in the spaces.

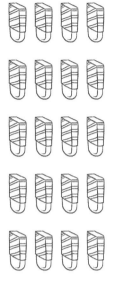

a Miya has ___20___ rubbers.

b She puts the rubbers equally into 5 boxes.
She puts the same number in each box.
How many rubbers are there in each box? ___4___

c She puts the rubbers equally into 4 boxes.
She puts the same number in each box.
How many rubbers are there in each box? ___5___

d She puts 10 rubbers into each box.
How many boxes does she need? ___2___

e She puts 4 rubbers into each box.
How many boxes does she need? ___5___

d Meena has 18 marbles.
She shares them equally among some children.
Each child gets 3 marbles.
How many children are there?

There are ___6___ children.

e Mrs Green has a farm.
There are 16 chickens.
She put 8 chickens in one coop.
How many coops does she need?

She needs ___2___ coops.

Date: _____

## Problem Solving

1 There are 8 squares and 12 triangles.

▢ ▢ ▢     △ △ △ △ △ △
▢ ▢ ▢     △ △ △ △ △ △
▢ ▢

Put an equal number of each shape into each group.

**a** I can put them into 2 groups.

There are __4__ squares and __6__ triangles in
each group.

There are __10__ shapes altogether in each group.

**b** I can put them into 4 groups.

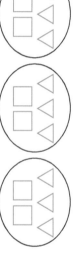

There are __2__ squares and __3__ triangles in
each group.

There are __5__ shapes altogether in each group.

**Unit 15:** Division

| Week | Learning Objectives | Thinking Skills | Resources |
|---|---|---|---|
| 2 | **(1) Telling the time to the hour**<br><br>Pupils will be able to:<br>• use the term 'o'clock' to tell the time to the hour and describe the position of the hour hand and of the minute hand<br>• read and show the time to the hour on a clock<br>• show the times on the clock for activities | • Relating (time and clock shown)<br>• Relating (time and event) | • Pupil Textbook 1B, pp 84 to 85<br>• Practice Book 1D, pp 21 to 26<br>• Teacher's Guide 1B, pp 158 to 159 |
| 2 | **(2) Telling the time to the half hour**<br><br>Pupils will be able to:<br>• use the term 'half past' to tell the time to the half hour and recognise that the minute hand is at 6<br>• read the time to half past the hour for different activities by looking at the clock shown next to each activity and arrange the events according to the time | • Relating (time and clock shown)<br>• Relating (time and event)<br>• Sequencing | • Pupil Textbook 1B, pp 86 to 89<br>• Practice Book 1D, pp 27 to 31<br>• Teacher's Guide 1B, pp 160 to 163 |
| 2 | *Put On Your Thinking Caps!*<br><br>Pupils will be able to:<br>• recognise that the hour and minute hands can be at 6 and any time of the day by demonstrating it using a clock<br>• discover the time the minute hand and the hour hand will be on top of each other using a clock | • Analysing parts and whole<br><br>Heuristic for problem solving:<br>• Act it out | • Pupil Textbook 1B, pp 90<br>• Practice Book 1D, pp 32 to 33<br>• Teacher's Guide 1B 164 |
| | Review 6 | | • Practice Book 1D, pp 35 to 38 |

**Summative assessment opportunity**

Assessment Book 1, Test 7, pp 91 to 99

# Time

## Learning objectives:
## Telling the time to the hour

**Pupils will be able to:**

- use the term 'o'clock' to tell the time to the hour and describe the position of the hour hand and of the minute hand

- read and show the time to the hour on a clock

- show the times on the clock for activities

## Teaching sequence

- Show pupils the clock and ask them questions about it.
  *"What is the clock for?"*
  *"What do you see on the face of the clock?"*
  *"How many numbers are there on the face of the clock?"*
  *"What time does school begin/ does school end?"*
  Ask pupils to read the numbers on the clock.

- Show pupils the demonstration clock with its hands at 1 o'clock. Tell them the time and write '1 o'clock' on the board.

- Repeat the activity to teach the times from 2 o'clock to 12 o'clock. Invite volunteers to position the hands of the clock as you teach. Point out to pupils that the minute hand is always at the number '12' when the term 'o'clock' is used.

- Tell pupils that from 1 o'clock in the morning, the hands of the clock move to 12 o'clock at noon. After that, the hands of the clock move to 1 o'clock in the afternoon until 12 o'clock at midnight.

- Discuss possible activities that people do at a certain time in the morning and at the same time at night.

## Key concept

Time can be used to measure the duration of an event

## Thinking skills

- Relating (time and clock shown)

- Relating (time and event)

## What you will need

Large clock with movable hour and minute hands (see Photocopy master 4 on page 287)

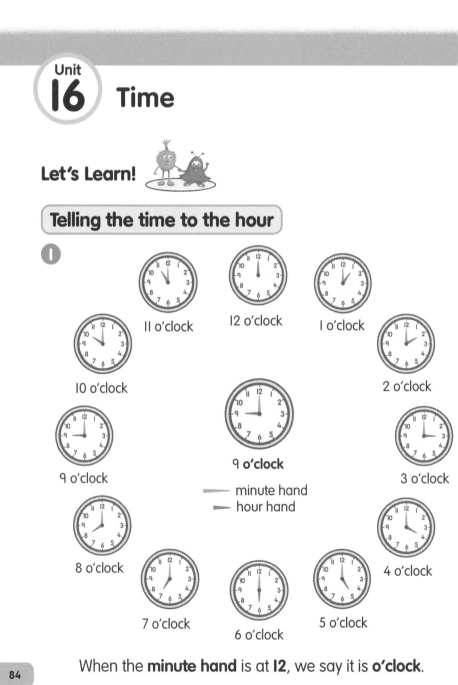

## What you will need

- Large clock with movable hour and minute hands (see Photocopy master 4 on page 287)
- Hour and minute hands cut from Photocopy master 4 (see page 287)
- Paper plate with markings at numbers and slit in the centre of plate to fasten hands
- Split pins
- Cardboard, glue, hole punch, adhesive tape, colour pencils or pens and scissors for each group

## Independent work

Practice 1 in Practice Book 1D, pp 21 to 26.

---

Time  **Unit 16**

**2** It's now 12 o'clock.    No, it's 5 o'clock.

Peter    Miya

Who is correct? Miya

**Activity**

**3  a**  Use a paper plate, split pin and two clock hands to make your own clock.

Then put on the numbers.

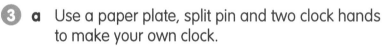

Now use your clock to show these times.

2 o'clock     8 o'clock     12 o'clock
  5 o'clock         9 o'clock

**b**  Use the clock to show the time you do the following.

Wake up     Eat dinner     Go to bed

Eat lunch

Answers vary

Practice Book 1D, p.21

85

---

## Teaching sequence

**2**

- Show a time on the clock and state the correct or an incorrect time, then ask pupils to tell you whether the time stated is correct. Ask a volunteer to write the correct time on the board.
- Repeat the activity by showing different times on the clock to assess pupils' understanding.

**3**

**a**

- Ask pupils to write the numbers '1' to '12' on their paper plates in the places indicated with markings.
- Show pupils how to punch a hole into the hour and minute hands of the clock and insert a split pin through the hour and minute hands.
- Then insert the split pin through the hole in the middle of the plate and fix it in place.
- Encourage pupils to decorate and personalise their clocks.
- Ask pupils in each group to show different times with their clocks and say what they would be doing at those times:
  *"I eat lunch at 12 o'clock."*
  *"I go to bed at 8 o'clock."*

**b**

- Ask pupils to show the times when they usually carry out these activities.

**Unit 16:** Time    **159**

## Learning objectives: Telling the time to the half hour

**Pupils will be able to:**

- use the term 'half past' to tell the time to the half hour and recognise that the minute hand is at 6

- read the time to half past the hour for different activities by looking at the clock shown next to each activity and arrange the events according to the time

## Key concept

Measuring half an hour using the term 'half past'

## What you will need

Large clock with movable hour and minute hands (see Photocopy master 4 on page 287)

## Teaching sequence

- Revise the concept of 'o'clock' with pupils by showing 7 o'clock on the clock.

- Move the minute hand to '6'. Tell pupils that when the minute hand is at 6, it shows 'half past'. Write the time 'half past 7' on the board.

- Point out to pupils that the position of the hour hand is halfway between 7 and 8.

- Explain the strategy to read the time given as 'half past':

  **Step 1**: Read the hour hand.

  If it is between two numbers, choose the preceding number.

  **Step 2**: Read the minute hand.

  If it is pointing at 6, it is read as half past.

  **Step 3**: Read the indicated hour and minute together.

- Ask pupils to show the same time on their clocks.

Unit 16  Time

## Let's Learn!

### Telling the time to the half hour

1  Millie wakes up at 7 o'clock.

Millie eats breakfast at **half past** 7.

When the **minute hand** is at **6**, we say it is **half past**.

The hour hand has moved too!

86

## Thinking skills

- Relating (time and clock shown)
- Relating (time and event)
- Sequencing

## Additional activities

- Call out various times and ask volunteers to show them on their clocks. You could also show a certain time and ask volunteers to tell the time.
- Ask pupils to discuss their usual mealtimes. Ask them to show the times of these meals on the clock and write the times on the board.

Peter feeds his cat at

half past 8

in the morning.

The children play at

half past 4

in the afternoon.

Ella reads a story at

half past 7

at night.

87

## Teaching sequence

**2** to **4**

- Assess pupils' ability to write the time using 'half past'.
- Encourage pupils to use the strategy shown in **1** to work on the questions. For pupils who need additional support, provide vocabulary cards.
- Ask pupils to look at the clocks and the times shown for the different activities and to record the times shown.
- Encourage pupils to discuss what they normally do during the times shown in the pictures.

**Teaching sequence**

- Ask pupils to work in groups to decide on the order of the pictures.
- Ask pupils to look at the pictures and encourage them to read out the times on the clocks shown. This will give them clues for the sequence of events in the story of Jack and his mum.

**Independent work**
Practice 2 and *Maths Journal* in
Practice Book 1D, pp 27 to 31.

Time **Unit 16**

## Activity

**a** Where are Jack and his
mum at 3 o'clock?
Jack's mum is playing a game.
Jack is eating popcorn.

**b** What time does Jack's
mum win the game?
At half past 3.

**c** What happens at 4 o'clock?
Jack and his mum meet Farha.

**d** Does Jack's mum buy him
a balloon at half past 4?
No

**e** What do you think
happens at half past 5?
Answers vary.
Example: Jack and his mum go
home happily.

Practice Book 1D, p.27

89

## Teaching sequence

**a** to **e**

- Ask pupils to answer the
questions.
- Encourage pupils to think of as
many possible endings to the
story as they can.

## Objectives of activity

Pupils will be able to:

- recognise that the hour and minute hands can be at 6 and any time of the day by demonstrating it using a clock
- discover the time the minute hand and the hour hand will be on top of each other using a clock

## What you will need

A clock

## Thinking skill

Analysing parts and whole

## Heuristic for problem solving

Act it out

## Independent work

*Challenging Practice* and Review 6 in Practice Book ID, pp 32 to 38.

## Teaching sequence

**6** *Put On Your Thinking Caps!*

**a**

- Ask pupils to read what Googol says about the position of the hour hand and the minute hand at 6:30.
- Ask pupils to use a clock to find the answer.

**b**

- Encourage pupils to guess the time when the minute hand and the hour hand are on top of each other.
- Encourage pupils to try this out using a clock.

---

## Put On Your Thinking Caps!

**6** **a**   At half past 6, the hour hand and the minute hand are pointing to the number 6.

Is this correct? No.

Why?
The hour hand should point between the numbers 6 and 7.

**b**   What time will it be when the minute hand and the hour hand are on top of each other? 12 o'clock

Practice Book ID, p.32

90

# Unit 16 Time

Date: _____

## Practice 1  Telling the time to the hour

1  Match the clock to the correct time.

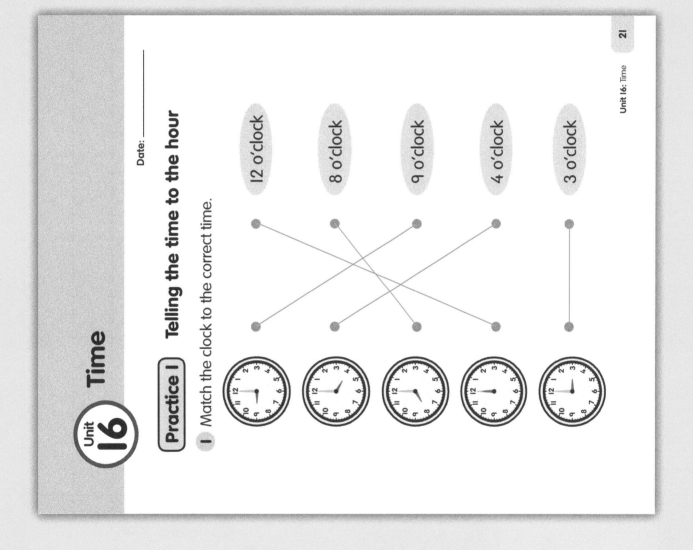

12 o'clock

8 o'clock

9 o'clock

4 o'clock

3 o'clock

**2** This is what Millie does on Monday. Fill in the spaces.

**a** She brushes her teeth at __7 o'clock__.

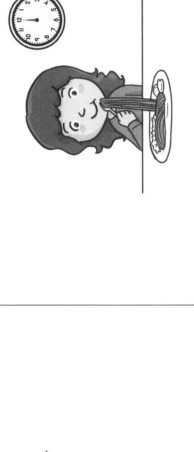

**b** School starts at __9 o'clock__.

**c** She has lunch at __12 o'clock__.

**d** She plays with her friends at __3 o'clock__.

**g** She eats dinner at _____6 o'clock_____ .

**h** She goes to bed at _____8 o'clock_____ .

**e** She plays the piano at _____4 o'clock_____ .

**f** She reads a book at _____5 o'clock_____ .

## Practice 2  Telling the time to the half hour

**1** Match the clock to the correct time.

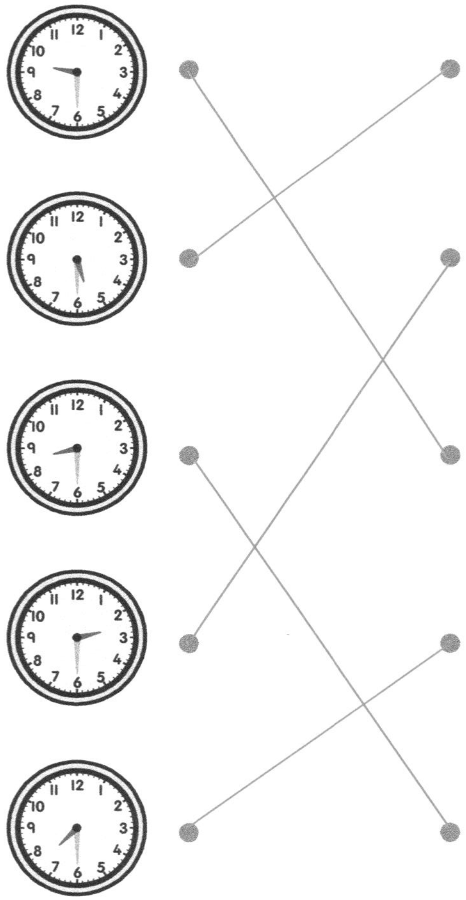

half past 5

half past 2

half past 9

half past 7

half past 8

---

**3** Colour the clock faces that show the correct time.

3 o'clock

9 o'clock

12 o'clock

5 o'clock

11 o'clock

a

b

c

d

e

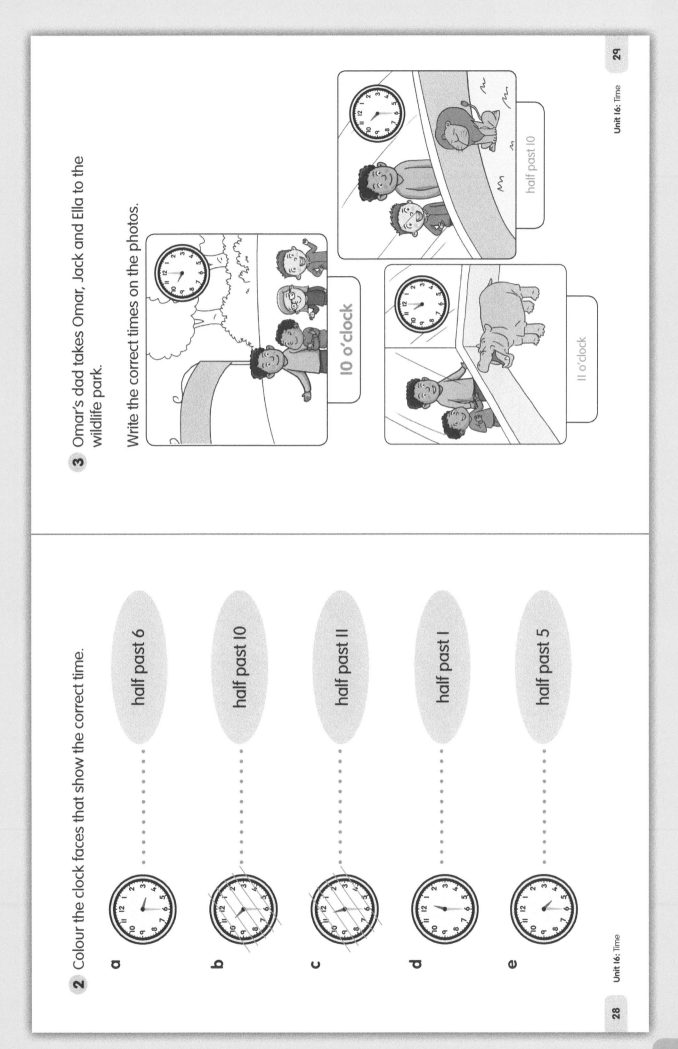

3 Omar's dad takes Omar, Jack and Ella to the wildlife park.

Write the correct times on the photos.

10 o'clock

11 o'clock

half past 10

2 Colour the clock faces that show the correct time.

half past 6

half past 10

half past 11

half past 1

half past 5

a

b

c

d

e

Date: _____

## Maths Journal

1. What do you do every day at the times shown?
   Use **o'clock** or **half past** in your sentences. Answers vary

What I do in the morning ...

_____

_____

What I do in the afternoon ...

_____

_____

What I do at night ...

_____

_____

half past 11

half past 12

1 o'clock

True

True

False

True

Picture D

Read each sentence carefully.
Then write **True** or **False**.

**a** At 8 o'clock Ruby helps to pack a picnic.

**b** Ruby and her friends have lunch at half past 12.

**c** They play a game at half past 7.

**d** Ruby walks home with her mum at half past 4.

---

Date: _____

## Challenging Practice

I  Ruby had a busy day.
Here are some pictures.

Picture A

Picture B

Picture C

# Review 6

Date: _____

**1** Tai has 6 pillows.
He puts 2 pillows on each bed.
How many beds are there?

There are __3__ beds.

**2** There are 9 oranges.
Circle 3 oranges to make 1 group.
How many groups of 3 oranges are there?

There are __3__ groups of 3 oranges.

**3** Some children share 20 apples equally.
Each child gets 5 apples.
How many children are there?

There are __4__ children.

7 Anna has 12 flowers.

a She puts the flowers in 3 vases.
How many flowers are there in each vase? _____ 4

b She puts 3 flowers in each vase.
How many vases does she need? _____ 4

c She puts 4 flowers in each vase.
How many vases does she need? _____ 3

8 Match the clocks to the correct times.

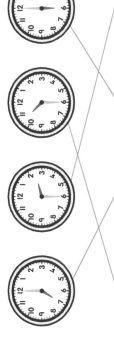

half past 10   7 o'clock   6 o'clock   half past 2

4 There are 8 strawberries.
The strawberries are divided equally between 2 children.
How many strawberries does each child get?

Each child gets _____ 4 strawberries.

5 12 sandwiches are divided equally between 3 children.
How many sandwiches will each child get?

Each child gets _____ 4 sandwiches.

6 16 toy robots are put equally into 4 boxes.
How many toy robots are in each box?

Each box has _____ 4 toy robots.

**9** Write the time for each activity.

**a**

Hardeep eats his breakfast at _____8 o'clock_____.

**b**

Hardeep plays football at ___half past 3___.

**c**

Hardeep reads his book at ___half past 7___.

**10** Which clock shows the correct time? Put a tick (✔) in the ☐.

**a**

10 o'clock ☐

**b**

half past 4 ☑

# Unit 17: Numbers to 100

Medium-term plan

| Week | Learning Objectives | Thinking Skills | Resources |
|---|---|---|---|
| 3 | **(1) Counting**<br><br>Pupils will be able to:<br>• recognise, read and write numbers up to 100 and the corresponding number words and concrete representations<br>• count within 100 by making tens first<br>• recognise and interpret sentences associated with tens and ones | • Analysing parts and whole | • Pupil Textbook 1B, pp 91 to 93<br>• Practice Book 1D, pp 39 to 40<br>• Teacher's Guide 1B, pp 179 to 181 |
| 3 | **(2) Place value**<br><br>Pupils will be able to:<br>• represent numbers as tens and ones in a place value chart<br>• show concrete representations in tens and ones given a number to 100<br>• write numerals given a set of concrete representations and vice versa with or without a place value chart | • Analysing parts and whole | • Pupil Textbook 1B, p 94<br>• Practice Book 1D, pp 41 to 44<br>• Teacher's Guide 1B, p 182 |

# Unit 17: Numbers to 100

| Week | Learning Objectives | Thinking Skills | Resources |
|---|---|---|---|
| 3 | **(3) Comparing, order and pattern**<br><br>Pupils will be able to:<br><br>• use a 'comparing tens and then ones' strategy to compare numbers to 100<br><br>• compare numbers to 100 using the terms 'greater than'/'greatest' and 'smaller than'/'smallest' with or without concrete representation<br><br>• compare numbers to 100 using the terms 'more than' and 'less than' with or without concrete representation<br><br>• arrange numbers in ascending or descending order | • Comparing<br>• Induction | • Pupil Textbook IB, pp 95 to 101<br>• Practice Book ID, pp 45 to 48<br>• Teacher's Guide IB, pp 183 to 189 |
| 4 | **(4) Simple addition**<br><br>Pupils will be able to:<br><br>• add a 2-digit number and a 1-digit number without regrouping<br><br>• add a 2-digit number and another 2-digit number without regrouping<br><br>• use the 'counting on' strategy to add<br><br>• use the number bond strategy to add<br><br>• use the addition strategy by adding the ones first, followed by the tens | • Analysing parts and whole | • Pupil Textbook IB, pp 102 to 105<br>• Practice Book ID, pp 49 to 52<br>• Teacher's Guide IB, pp 190 to 193 |

# Unit 17: Numbers to 100

| Week | Learning Objectives | Thinking Skills | Resources |
|---|---|---|---|
| 4 | **(5) More addition**<br><br>Pupils will be able to:<br>• add a 2-digit number and a 1-digit number with regrouping<br>• add a 2-digit number and another 2-digit number with regrouping<br>• use the number bond strategy to add<br>• use the 'making ten' strategy to add<br>• apply the regrouping concept in addition | • Analysing parts and whole | • Pupil Textbook 1B, pp 106 to 109<br>• Practice Book 1D, pp 53 to 58<br>• Teacher's Guide 1B, pp 194 to 197 |
| 4–5 | **(6) Simple subtraction**<br><br>Pupils will be able to:<br>• subtract a 1-digit number from a 2-digit number without regrouping<br>• subtract a 2-digit number from another 2-digit number without regrouping<br>• use the 'counting back' strategy to subtract<br>• use the 'taking away' strategy to subtract<br>• use the number bond strategy to subtract | • Analysing parts and whole | • Pupil Textbook, pp 110 to 114<br>• Practice Book 1D, pp 59 to 62<br>• Teacher's Guide 1B, pp 198 to 202 |

# Unit 17: Numbers to 100

| Week | Learning Objectives | Thinking Skills | Resources |
|------|--------------------|-----------------| ----------|
| 5 | **(7) More subtraction**<br><br>Pupils will be able to:<br>• subtract a 1-digit number from a 2-digit number with regrouping<br>• subtract a 2-digit number from another 2-digit number with regrouping<br>• apply the regrouping concept in subtraction<br>• use the number bond strategy to subtract | • Analysing parts and whole | • Pupil Textbook 1B, pp 115 to 119<br>• Practice Book 1D, pp 63 to 68<br>• Teacher's Guide 1B, pp 203 to 207 |
| 5 | *Put On Your Thinking Caps!*<br><br>Pupils will be able to use the number bond strategy to connect numbers to make addition and subtraction sentences up to 100. | • Deduction<br>• Identifying patterns and relationships<br><br>Heuristics for problem solving:<br>• Simplify the problem<br>• Guess and check | • Pupil Textbook 1B, p 120<br>• Practice Book 1D, pp 69 to 70<br>• Teacher's Guide 1B, p 208 |

# Numbers to 100

**Learning objectives: Counting**

**Pupils will be able to:**

- recognise, read and write numbers up to 100 and the corresponding number words and concrete representations
- count within 100 by making tens first
- recognise and interpret sentences associated with tens and ones

**Key concepts**

- Using one-to-one correspondence in counting
- 1 ten is the same as 10 ones
- 10 tens is 100

**Thinking skill**

Analysing parts and whole

**What you will need**

100 counters, e.g., cubes, straws

**Teaching sequence**

**1**

- Count out and organise twenty counters into groups of tens.
- Ask volunteers to do the same, counting out loud as they make tens using ten, twenty, thirty and forty counters.

**2**

- Show pupils 5 tens, 6 tens, 7 tens, 8 tens, 9 tens and 10 tens by counting out and grouping the counters as done above.
- Then introduce the numerals 50, 60, 70, 80, 90, 100 and their corresponding words. Ask pupils to follow and read aloud.

---

**Unit 17  Numbers to 100**

**Let's Learn!**

**Counting**

**1** Count the sticks.

10 sticks = 1 ten     → ten

20 sticks = 2 tens    twenty

**2** Count the bundles of 10.

> 10, … 20, … 30, … 40, … 50

5 tens ............... **50** ............... fifty

6 tens ............... **60** ............... sixty

7 tens ............... **70** ............... seventy

91

## What you will need

Base ten equipment

## Additional activity

Ask pupils to work in pairs.

Pupil A shows some rods and cubes e.g. 74: 7 tens and 4 ones. Pupil B counts how much is shown.

Pupils A and B swap roles.

## Teaching sequence

- Use cubes to show 53 by counting on in tens and ones.
- Show the number again by counting using rods and cubes.
- Ask volunteers to count out the rods and cubes.

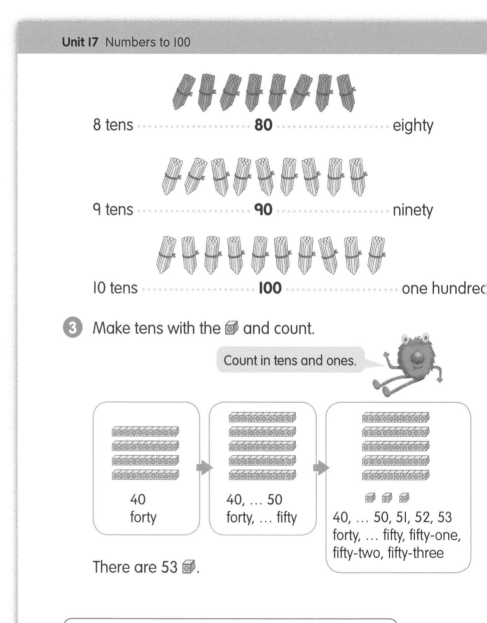

8 tens ·········· **80** ·········· eighty

9 tens ·········· **90** ·········· ninety

10 tens ·········· **100** ·········· one hundred

**3** Make tens with the 🎲 and count.

Count in tens and ones.

40
forty

40, ... 50
forty, ... fifty

40, ... 50, 51, 52, 53
forty, ... fifty, fifty-one, fifty-two, fifty-three

There are 53 🎲.

Home Maths — Using a Snakes & Ladders board, ask your child to count from 1 to 25. Then ask other friends or family members to continue to count the next 25 numbers until the last player reaches 100.

92

## Additional activities

- Ask pupils to work in groups of 3.

  Pupil A calls out a number, e.g., 68. Pupils B and C take turns to write down statements that express 68 in another way. For example, they are expected to write:

  *60 and 8 make 68*

  *60 + 8 = 68*

  Pupil A checks their answers and the pupils swap roles.

## Independent work

Practice I in Practice Book ID, pp 39 to 40.

## Teaching sequence

- Look for pupils who can count numbers up to I00.
- Ask them to write in numerals and in words.
- Check that pupils are counting in tens and ones, as some may still resort to counting in ones to find the answers.

- Introduce various ways to show numbers from 40 to I00 using concrete representations.
- Show pupils how to express 74 in various ways:

  *70 and 4 make 74*

  *70 + 4 = 74*

  *4 and 70 make 74*

  *4 + 70 = 74*

- Ask pupils to work on the questions shown in the textbook. Look for pupils who can add the tens and ones.

---

**4**

 Twenty, ... thirty, ... forty, ... seventy-one, ...

20, ... 30, ... 40, ... 50 , ... 60 , ... 70

7I, 72 , 73 , 74 , 75

There are 75 .

**5**

 I have 74 .

70 + 4 = 74

 70 and 4 make 74.

**6** Find the missing numbers.

a   50 + 4 = 54

b   60 and 7 make 67 .

c   7 and 70 make 77 .

d   80 and 2 make 82 .

e   3 and 90 make 93 .

f   9 + 90 = 99

> **Practice Book ID, p.39**

93

## Learning objectives: Place value

**Pupils will be able to:**

- represent numbers as tens and ones in a place value chart
- show concrete representations in tens and ones given a number to 100
- write numerals given a set of concrete representations and vice versa with or without a place value chart

## Key concept

Numbers to 100 can be represented as tens and ones in a place value chart.

## Thinking skill

Analysing parts and whole

## What you will need

- 100 counters, e.g. straws or cubes
- Base ten equipment

## Independent work

Practice 2 in Practice Book ID, pp 41 to 44.

## Teaching sequence

- Use the rods and cubes to count up to 98.
- Introduce the concept of 9 tens and 8 ones with the help of a place value chart. Link it to the concepts covered earlier:

    *90 and 8 make 98*

    *98 is 90 and 8*

    *98 is 9 tens 8 ones*

- Show the numeral expression:

    *98 = 90 and 8*

- Check pupils' understanding by asking them to complete the place value chart and place value sentence given concrete representations of 87.
- Use other numbers such as 69 to further assess their understanding.

- Ask pupils to work in small groups.
- Give different numbers to each group and ask them to present the numbers using concrete representations such as straws or cubes.

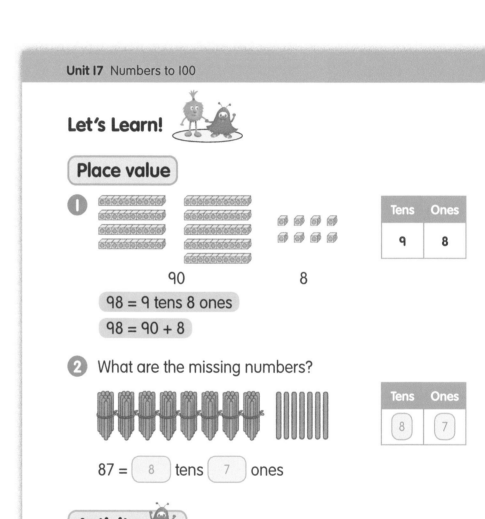

## Learning objectives: Comparing, order and pattern

**Pupils will be able to:**

- use a 'comparing tens and then ones' strategy to compare numbers to 100
- compare numbers to 100 using the terms 'greater than'/'greatest' and 'smaller than'/'smallest' with or without concrete representation
- compare numbers to 100 using the terms 'more than' and 'less than' with or without concrete representation
- arrange numbers in ascending or descending order

## Key concepts

- Numbers to 100 can be compared using the terms 'greater than' and 'smaller than'
- Numbers to 100 can be arranged in ascending or descending order

## Thinking skills

- Comparing
- Induction

# Let's Learn!

### Comparing, order and pattern

**①** You can count using this number track.

2 more                                                            2 less

| 50 | 51 | 52 | 53 | 54 | 55 | 56 | 57 | 58 | 59 | 60 | 61 | 62 | 63 | 64 | 65 |

Count on from 53.                    Count back from 65.

55 is 2 more than 53.             63 is 2 less than 65.
55 is greater than 53.           63 is smaller than 65.

**②**

10   10   10

I have 60 jelly beans.

10   10   10

60

3 more than 60 is [ 63 ].

3 less than 60 is [ 57 ].

95

## What you will need

Number track or number line

## Teaching sequence

**①**

- Show a number track with numbers from 50 to 65. Revise the concepts of 'more than', 'less than', 'how many more than', 'how many less than', 'greater than' and 'smaller than' using the number track.
- Work through the examples with reference to the 'counting on' and 'counting back' strategies.
- Point out to pupils that they are comparing two numbers. They can use the term 'more than' or 'less than' in comparing numbers.
- Ask pupils to use statements such as:

  To compare 53 and 55, we can say:

  *53 is 2 less than 55, or*
  *55 is 2 more than 53.*

- Compare 63 and 65 and ask pupils to read out the two statements.

**②**

- Assess pupils' understanding using this example.
- Ask them to read the statements and then refer to numbers on a number track to find the answers.

## What you will need

- Spinner A, labelled in steps of one from I to 9
- Spinner B, labelled in steps of ten from I0 to 90 (see Photocopy master 5 on page 288)
- Number track

## Teaching sequence

- Ask pupils to do this activity to practise using the 'more than' and 'less than' concepts.
- Ask pupils to write sentences using the numbers they get.
- Encourage pupils to use a number track.

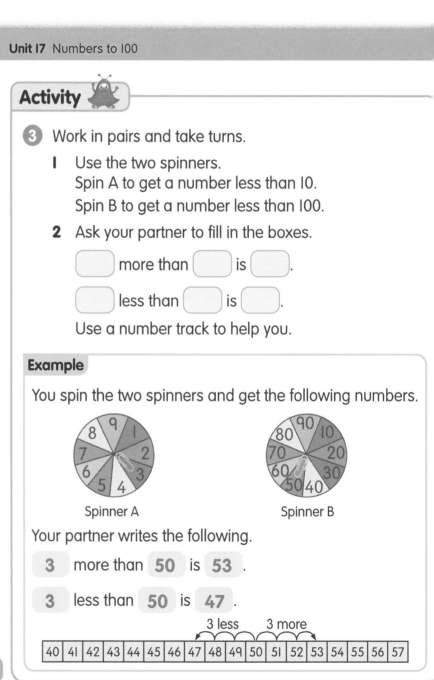

### Activity

3  Work in pairs and take turns.

I  Use the two spinners.
Spin A to get a number less than I0.
Spin B to get a number less than I00.

2  Ask your partner to fill in the boxes.

⬚ more than ⬚ is ⬚ .

⬚ less than ⬚ is ⬚ .

Use a number track to help you.

**Example**

You spin the two spinners and get the following numbers.

Spinner A

Spinner B

Your partner writes the following.

**3** more than **50** is **53** .

**3** less than **50** is **47** .

3 less    3 more

| 40 | 41 | 42 | 43 | 44 | 45 | 46 | 47 | 48 | 49 | 50 | 51 | 52 | 53 | 54 | 55 | 56 | 57 |

96

Numbers to 100 **Unit 17**

**4** Compare 60 and 59.

The tens are different.

Compare the tens. 6 tens is greater than 5 tens.

| Tens | Ones |
|------|------|
| 6 | 0 |

60

| Tens | Ones |
|------|------|
| 5 | 9 |

59

60 is greater than 59.

**5** Compare 67 and 69.

The tens are the same. We compare the ones.

Compare the ones. 7 is smaller than 9.

| Tens | Ones |
|------|------|
| 6 | 7 |

67

| Tens | Ones |
|------|------|
| 6 | 9 |

69

67 is smaller than 69.

97

## Teaching sequence

**4**

- Show the numbers 60 and 59 on place value charts with concrete representations using base ten equipment.
- Work through the steps to find out which number is greater or smaller:

  **Step 1**: Compare the tens.

  **Step 2**: Compare the ones.
- Point out that the 6 tens from 60 is greater than 5 tens from 59. So 60 is greater than 59. There is no need to go on to the second step.
- You could place the two numbers vertically as an alternative method for comparing numbers.

| Tens | Ones |
|------|------|
| 6 | 0 |
| 5 | 9 |

**5**

- Repeat the steps above using 67 and 69. Point out that in this example, the 6 tens from 67 is the same as 6 tens of 69.
- We move on to the next step to compare the ones. 7 ones from 67 is less than 9 ones from 69. So 67 is less than 69.
- Similarly, you can arrange the numbers vertically before comparing.

Ask pupils to work in pairs.

Pupil A calls out a number that is less than 100. Pupil B calls out another number that is greater or smaller than the given number. Pupil A says which number is greater and which is smaller, and explains why.

Pupils A and B swap roles.

## Teaching sequence

- Ask pupils to arrange the two numbers in the vertical column format.

| Tens | Ones |
|------|------|
| 7 | 2 |
| 5 | 6 |

- Point out that the tens are different. 7 tens from 72 is greater than 5 tens from 56. Pupils should be able to conclude that 56 is smaller than 72 or 72 is greater than 56.
- Encourage pupils to think aloud when they are solving the problem.

- Ask pupils to attempt the question before discussing with the class. Again, ask pupils to arrange the numbers in the vertical column format before comparing numbers.

| Tens | Ones |
|------|------|
| 8 | 7 |
| 8 | 4 |

- The tens are the same, therefore compare the ones.
- 7 ones from 87 is greater than 4 ones from 84. Pupils should conclude that 87 is greater than 84 or 84 is smaller than 87.

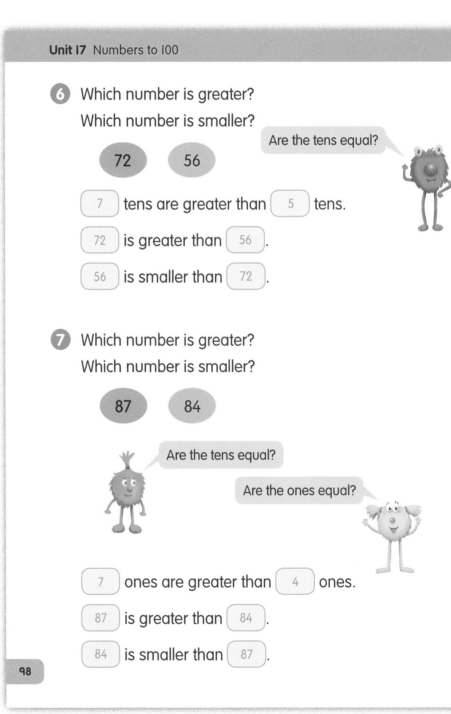

Unit 17  Numbers to 100

6 Which number is greater?
Which number is smaller?

72    56

Are the tens equal?

7 tens are greater than 5 tens.

72 is greater than 56.

56 is smaller than 72.

7 Which number is greater?
Which number is smaller?

87    84

Are the tens equal?

Are the ones equal?

7 ones are greater than 4 ones.

87 is greater than 84.

84 is smaller than 87.

98

Base ten equipment

**Additional activity**

Ask pupils to work in pairs.

Pupil A calls out a number that is less than 100. Pupil B calls out two numbers, either greater or smaller than the original number, and writes down the three numbers on the board. Pupil A says which is the greatest number and which is the smallest number and explains why.

Pupils A and B swap roles.

---

Numbers to 100 **Unit 17**

**8** Compare 68, 83 and 95.

Which is the smallest number?

Which is the greatest number?

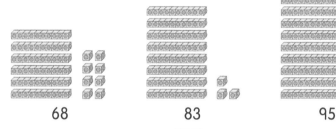

68          83          95

The smallest number is 68 .

The greatest number is 95 .

 Why is it the smallest?

Why is 95 greater than 83?

**9** Find the greatest number.

Find the smallest number.

a  84    48    100    100, 48

b  56    59    58    59, 56

99

---

**Teaching sequence**

**8**

- Revise the strategy of comparing 3 numbers with pupils.
- Show the numbers 68, 83 and 95 using base ten equipment.
- Work through the steps to compare the numbers:

  **Step 1**: Compare the tens. Point out that 68 is the smallest because 6 tens is smaller than 8 tens from 83 and 9 tens from 95. Then explain that 95 is the greatest because 9 tens is greater than 8 tens and 6 tens.

  **Step 2**: Compare the ones. Explain that there is no need to compare the ones as the order of the numbers has been determined by comparing the tens.

**9**

- Ask pupils to work on these examples. Encourage them to use any methods given above.

## Additional activity

Ask pupils to work in pairs.

Encourage pupils to design a number track similar to the one in the textbook. Ask them to swap their number tracks and complete the unknown numbers.

## Teaching sequence

- Show the number track with the three missing numbers. Explain that the numbers on the track are arranged in a pattern. Work through the strategy to help them find the missing numbers:

**Step 1**: Check any two given adjacent numbers and use the 'more than' or 'less than' concept to find the difference between them.

**Step 2**: Check with other sets of adjacent numbers to confirm that the difference between them gives the same number.

**Step 3**: Use this 'difference' to find the unknown numbers.

Show the strategy by using the following numbers taken from the number track:

60 is 5 more than 55.

95 is 5 more than 90.

So the difference is 5.

5 more than 65 is 70.

So the first unknown number is 70.

5 less than 90 is 85.

The second unknown number is 85.

5 more than 95 is 100.

So the third unknown number is 100.

- Ask pupils to solve the problem. Use the question to assess pupils' understanding.

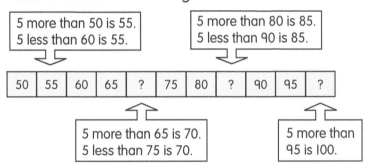

10 The numbers on this number track are arranged in a pattern.

Some numbers are missing.

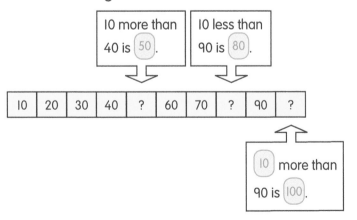

11 The numbers below are arranged in a pattern.

Find the missing numbers.

Work with your child to make some number patterns going up by 10 each time. See if they can make a number pattern starting from 85.

100

# Independent work

Practice 3 in Practice Book ID,
pp 45 to 48.

## Game

Players: 2 to 4

**12 What's my number?**

How to play:

1   Think of a number between 50 and 100.

2   The other players take turns to ask you questions
    to find the number.

3   You can answer only **Yes** or **No** to the questions.

4   See who guesses the right number first!

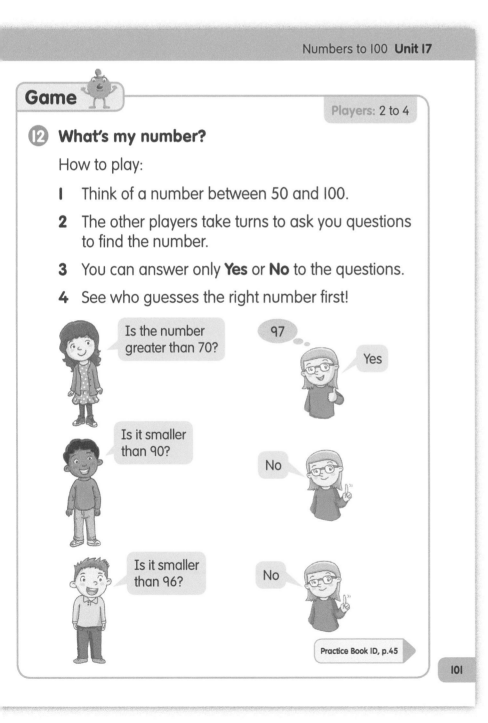

Is the number
greater than 70?

97

Yes

Is it smaller
than 90?

No

Is it smaller
than 96?

No

Practice Book ID, p.45

101

## Teaching sequence

**12** *Game*

• The objective of this game is
  to help pupils reinforce the
  'greater than' and 'smaller
  than' concepts.

• Encourage pupils to use
  both terms to determine the
  unknown number.

## Learning objectives:
## Simple addition

**Pupils will be able to:**

- add a 2-digit number and a 1-digit number without regrouping
- add a 2-digit number and another 2-digit number without regrouping
- use the 'counting on' strategy to add
- use the number bond strategy to add
- use the addition strategy by adding the ones first, followed by the tens

## Teaching sequence

**a**

- Introduce the 'counting on' strategy using a number track or number line. Explain to pupils that this strategy is efficient when the one-digit is small, as it is in this question.

**b**

- Introduce and explain the vertical addition strategy using a place value chart. Notice that no regrouping is needed in this section. Show and explain the following strategy using vertical addition:
  **Step 1**: Add the ones.
  5 ones from 75 and 4 ones make 9 ones.
  Write the result in the ones column.
  **Step 2**: Add the tens.
  7 tens and 0 tens make 7 tens.
  Write the result in the tens column.
  The result is 7 tens and 9 ones which is 79.
- You can relate number bonds to this problem and add the corresponding tens and ones.
  E.g. 75 is 7 tens and 5 ones. 4 ones and 5 ones make 9 ones. So by combining them the result is 7 tens 9 ones which is 79.

## Key concept

The 'adding on' and 'part-whole' concepts are used in adding numbers

## What you will need

Base ten equipment

---

**Unit 17** Numbers to 100

**Let's Learn!**

**Simple addition**

There are different ways to get the answer.

**1**  75 + 4 = ?

**a**  Count on from 75.

| 75 | 76 | 77 | 78 | 79 |

75, **76, 77, 78, 79**

**b**  Use a place value chart.

| Tens | Ones |
|------|------|

75

4

First add the ones.

```
  Tens  Ones
    7     5
+         4
─────────────
          9
```

5 ones + 4 ones = 9 ones

Then add the tens.

```
  Tens  Ones
    7     5
+         4
─────────────
    7     9
```

7 tens + 0 tens = 7 tens

75 + 4

70    5

4 + 5 = 9
70 + 9 = 79

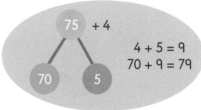

75 + 4 = 79

---

Additional activity

Ask pupils to work in pairs.

Pupil A calls out a 2-digit number up to 100 and a 1-digit number which is less than the ones of the 2-digit number. Pupil B adds the two numbers using any of the 3 methods given in **2**.

Pupils A and B swap roles.

**2** 82 + 5 = ?

**a** Count on from 82.

82, 83, 84, 85, 86, 87

**b** Use a place value chart.

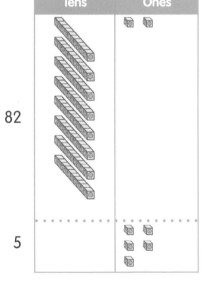

| Tens | Ones |
|------|------|

82

5

Tens  Ones

8   2
+     5
_____
8   7

First add the ones.
Then add the tens.

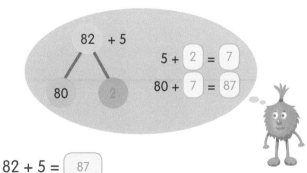

82 + 5

80    2

5 + 2 = 7
80 + 7 = 87

82 + 5 = 87

103

Teaching sequence

**2**

- Check whether pupils can apply the three strategies below to add a 1-digit number to a 2-digit number without regrouping.
  - 'Counting on' method
  - Vertical addition with a place value chart
  - Using number bonds
- Explain to pupils that they can use any of these strategies to solve the problems.

Ask pupils to work in pairs.

Pupil A calls out a 2-digit number less than 100 and a tens number. Pupil B adds the two numbers using any of the 3 methods given in .

Pupils A and B swap roles.

## Teaching sequence

- Introduce and explain the vertical addition strategy using a place value chart. Notice that no regrouping is needed in this section. Model and explain the following strategy using vertical addition:

**Step I**: Add the ones.
0 ones from 30 and 6 ones from 46 make 6 ones. Write the result in the ones column.

**Step 2**: Add the tens.
3 tens from 30 and 4 tens from 46 make 7 tens. Write the result in the tens column.
The result is 7 tens 6 ones which is 76.

- You can relate number bonds to this problem and add the corresponding tens and ones.
E.g. 4 tens and 3 tens make 7 tens. 6 ones and 0 ones make 6 ones.
So by combining them the result is 7 tens and 6 ones which is 76.

- Check whether pupils can apply either of the two strategies below to add tens to a 2-digit number without regrouping.
  ○ Vertical addition with a place value chart
  ○ Using number bonds

---

**Unit 17  Numbers to 100**

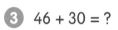 46 + 30 = ?

Use a place value chart.

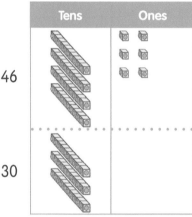

First add the ones.

| Tens | Ones |
|------|------|
| 4 | 6 |
| + 3 | 0 |
| | 6 |

6 ones + 0 ones = 6 ones

Then add the tens.

| Tens | Ones |
|------|------|
| 4 | 6 |
| + 3 | 0 |
| 7 | 6 |

4 tens + 3 tens = 7 tens

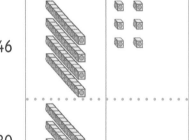
6 ones + 0 ones = 6 ones
4 tens + 3 tens = 7 tens
46 + 30 = 76

46 + 30 = 76

④ 50 + 40 = ?
First add the ones.

⌞0⌝ ones + ⌞0⌝ ones = ⌞0⌝ ones

Then add the tens.

⌞5⌝ tens + ⌞4⌝ tens = ⌞9⌝ tens

| Tens | Ones |
|------|------|
| 5 | 0 |
| + 4 | 0 |
| 9 | 0 |

50 + 40 = ⌞90⌝

104

---

Ask pupils to work in pairs.

Pupil A calls out two 2-digit numbers less than 100. The ones digit from both numbers should not add up to 10 or more. Pupil B adds the two numbers using any of the 3 methods given in ②.

Pupils A and B swap roles.

## Independent work

Practice 4 in Practice Book ID, pp 49 to 52.

**⑤** 42 + 56 = ?

Use a place value chart.

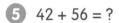

42 = 4 tens 2 ones
56 = 5 tens 6 ones

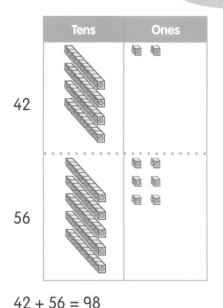

First add the ones.

Tens Ones

```
   4   2
 + 5   6
 ───────
       8
```

2 ones + 6 ones = 8 ones

Then add the tens.

Tens Ones

```
   4   2
 + 5   6
 ───────
   9   8
```

4 tens + 5 tens = 9 tens

42 + 56 = 98

**⑥** 43 + 36 = ?

First add the ones.

[ 3 ] ones + [ 6 ] ones = [ 9 ] ones

Then add the tens.

[ 4 ] tens + [ 3 ] tens = [ 7 ] tens

43 + 36 = [ 79 ]

Tens Ones

```
   4   3
 + 3   6
 ───────
   7   9
```

Practice Book ID, p.49

105

## Teaching sequence

**⑤**

- Introduce and explain the vertical addition strategy using a place value chart. Notice that no regrouping is needed in this section. Model and explain the following strategy using vertical addition:

  **Step 1**: Add the ones.
  2 ones from 42 and 6 ones from 56 make 8 ones. Write the result in the ones column.

  **Step 2**: Add the tens.
  4 tens from 42 and 5 tens from 56 make 9 tens. Write the result in the tens column.
  The result is 9 tens and 8 ones which is 98.

- You can relate number bonds to this problem and add the corresponding tens and ones.

**⑥**

- Check whether pupils can add two 2-digit numbers without regrouping, using both the vertical addition and the number bond strategies.

## Learning objectives: More addition

**Pupils will be able to:**

- add a 2-digit number and a 1-digit number with regrouping
- add a 2-digit number and another 2-digit number with regrouping
- use the number bond strategy to add
- use the 'making ten' strategy to add
- apply the regrouping concept in addition

## Key concepts

- The 'adding on' and 'part-whole' concepts are used in adding numbers
- The regrouping concept is applied in addition

## Thinking skill

Analysing parts and whole

## What you will need

Base ten equipment

## Teaching sequence

- Start the lesson with an activity to help pupils revise regrouping from ones to ten using base ten equipment.

  E.g. Pupils should be able to show that 4 ones and 9 ones make 13 ones and then regroup to 1 ten and 3 ones.

- Next introduce and explain the vertical addition strategy using a place value chart. Notice that regrouping is needed in this section. Model and explain the following strategy using vertical addition:

  **Step 1**: Add the ones.
  6 ones from 66 and 7 ones make 13 ones.
  13 = 1 ten 3 ones after regrouping.
  Write 3 ones in the ones column. The 1 ten is placed under the tens column.

  **Step 2**: Add the tens.
  6 tens and 1 ten (regrouped from ones) make 7 tens.
  Write the result in the tens column.
  The result is 7 tens 3 ones which is 73.

- Show the regrouping using concrete representation.

---

Unit 17 Numbers to 100

## Let's Learn!

**More addition**

1. 66 + 7 = ?
   Use a place value chart.

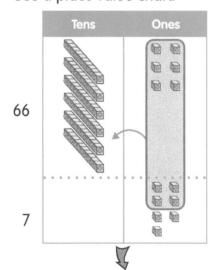

First add the ones.

6 ones + 7 ones = 13 ones

Regroup the ones.
13 ones = 1 ten 3 ones

Then add the tens.

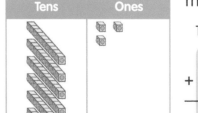

6 tens + 1 ten = 7 tens

106    66 + 7 = 73

---

**194**    Unit 17: Numbers to 100

**Additional activity**

Ask pupils to work in pairs.

Pupil A calls out a 2-digit number less than 100 and a I-digit number, so that the sum of the ones digits add up to 10 or more. Pupil B adds the two numbers.

Pupils A and B swap roles.

**Teaching sequence**

② 

- Check whether pupils can add a I-digit number to a 2-digit number with regrouping using vertical addition with a place value chart.
- For pupils who need additional support, provide concrete materials such as cubes.
- If necessary, go through the steps shown in **a**.

② **a**  62 + 9 = ?

First add the ones.

2 ones + 9 ones = [ 11 ] ones

Regroup the ones.

[ 11 ] ones = 1 ten [ 1 ] one

| Tens | Ones |
|------|------|
| 6 | 2 |
| + | 9 |
| 7 | 1 |

Then add the tens.

6 tens + [ 1 ] ten = [ 7 ] tens

62 + 9 = [ 71 ]

**b**
```
    5   6
+       8
    6   4
```

**c**
```
    3   6
+       5
    4   1
```

**d**
```
    7   8
+       5
    8   3
```

**e**
```
    8   9
+       4
    9   3
```

## Teaching sequence

- This activity provides more practice to add a 1-digit number to a 2-digit number with or without regrouping.

- Introduce and explain the vertical addition strategy using a place value chart. Notice that regrouping is needed in this section. Model and explain the following strategy using vertical addition:

**Step 1**: Add the ones.
8 ones from 18 and 3 ones from 33 make 11 ones.
11 ones = 1 ten 1 one after regrouping.
Write 1 one in the ones column. The 1 ten is placed under the tens column.

**Step 2**: Add the tens.
1 ten from 18, 3 tens from 33 and 1 ten (regrouped from ones) make 5.
Write the result in the tens column.
The result is 5 tens 1 one which is 51.

### Activity

3  Work in pairs.
You will need a spinner.

Spinner

1  Player 1 spins the spinner to get a number.

2  Player 1 adds this number to 52.

$52 + \boxed{\phantom{0}} = \boxed{\phantom{0}}$

3  Player 2 spins the spinner. Player 2 adds this number to 64.

$64 + \boxed{\phantom{0}} = \boxed{\phantom{0}}$

4  Together think of some more numbers to add to a spinner number.

4  $33 + 18 = ?$

$33 = 3$ tens 3 ones
$18 = 1$ ten 8 ones

| Tens | Ones |
|------|------|
| 33 | |
| 18 | |

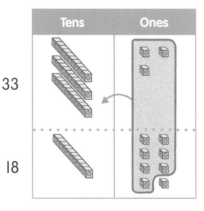

First add the ones.

| Tens | Ones |
|------|------|
| 3 | 3 |
| + 1 | 8 |
| | 1 |

3 ones + 8 ones = 11 ones

**Regroup the ones.**
11 ones = 1 ten 1 one

108

## What you will need
Spinner with segments numbered from 0 to 9 (see Photocopy master 6 on page 289)

## Additional activity
Pupils spin the spinner to get three numbers. They choose two of the numbers to make a 2-digit number. Then they add this number to the remaining 1-digit number.

Practice 5 and Practice 6 in
Practice Book ID, pp 53 to 58.

Numbers to 100 **Unit 17**

**Tens** | **Ones**

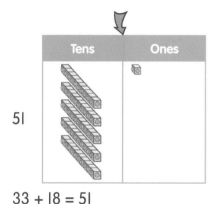

51

33 + 18 = 51

Then add the tens.

Tens   Ones

| | Tens | Ones |
|---|---|---|
| | 3 | 3 |
| + | 1 | 8 |
| | 5 | 1 |
| | 1 | |

3 tens + 1 ten + 1 ten = 5 tens

5 Add and regroup the numbers.

**a**   Tens   Ones

| | Tens | Ones |
|---|---|---|
| | 4 | 7 |
| + 3 | | 8 |
| | 8 | 5 |

First add the ones.

7 ones + 8 ones = 15 ones

Regroup the ones.

15 ones = 1 ten 5 ones

Then add the tens.

4 tens + 3 tens + 1 ten =

8 tens

**b**

| | 2 | 8 |
|---|---|---|
| + 1 | | 4 |
| | 4 | 2 |

**c**

| | 5 | 4 |
|---|---|---|
| + 2 | | 7 |
| | 8 | 1 |

**d**

| | 3 | 5 |
|---|---|---|
| + 3 | | 6 |
| | 7 | 1 |

**e**

| | 4 | 9 |
|---|---|---|
| + 2 | | 3 |
| | 7 | 2 |

Practice Book ID, pp.53 and 57    109

**Teaching sequence**

5

- Check whether pupils can add a 2-digit number to another 2-digit number with regrouping, using vertical addition with a place value chart.
- For pupils who need additional support, provide concrete materials such as cubes.
- If necessary, go through the steps in **a** with pupils before asking them to work on the remaining questions.

## Learning objectives:
## Simple subtraction

**Pupils will be able to:**

- subtract a 1-digit number from a 2-digit number without regrouping
- subtract a 2-digit number from another 2-digit number without regrouping
- use the 'counting back' strategy to subtract
- use the 'taking away' strategy to subtract
- use the number bond strategy to subtract

## Teaching sequence

**a**

- Introduce and explain the 'counting back' strategy using a number track. Explain to pupils that this strategy is efficient only when the number being subtracted is small.

**b**

- Introduce and explain the vertical subtraction strategy using a place value chart. Notice that no regrouping is needed in this section. Model and explain the following strategy using vertical subtraction:

  **Step 1**: Subtract the ones.
  8 ones – 3 ones = 5 ones
  Write the result in the ones column.
  **Step 2**: Subtract the tens.
  4 tens – 0 tens = 4 tens
  Write the result in the tens column.
  The result is 4 tens and 5 ones which is 45.

- You can relate number bonds to this problem and subtract the corresponding tens and ones.
  E.g. 48 → 4 tens and 8 ones
  4 tens – 0 tens = 4 tens
  8 ones – 3 ones = 5 ones
  So by combining them the result is 4 tens 5 ones which is 45.

## Key concept
The 'taking away' concept is used in subtraction.

## Thinking skill
Analysing parts and whole

## What you will need
Base ten equipment

---

**Unit 17** Numbers to 100

**Let's Learn!**

**Simple subtraction**

There are different ways to get the answer.

① 48 – 3 = ?

| 40 | 41 | 42 | 43 | 44 | 45 | 46 | 47 | 48 | 49 |

**a** Count back from 48.

48, **47, 46, 45**

**b** Use a place value chart.

First subtract the ones.

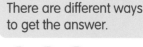

```
  Tens   Ones
    4      8
  -        3
  _____
           5
```

8 ones – 3 ones = 5 ones

Then subtract the tens.

```
  Tens   Ones
    4      8
  -        3
  _____
    4      5
```

4 tens – 0 tens = 4 tens

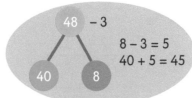

48 – 3 = 45

8 – 3 = 5
40 + 5 = 45

110

---

198      Unit 17: Numbers to 100

**2**  **a**  68 – 6 = 62

**b**  82 – 2 = 80

**3**  70 – 40 = ?

**a**  Count back from 70.

**b**  Use a place value chart.

70, ... 60, ... 50, ... 40, ... 30

| Tens | Ones |
|------|------|
| | |

70

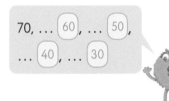

70 – 40

70 – 40 = 30

30 + 0 = 30

70   0

| Tens | Ones |
|------|------|
| | |

30

| Tens | Ones |
|------|------|
| 7 | 0 |
| – 4 | 0 |
| 3 | 0 |

First subtract the ones.
Then subtract the tens.

70 – 40 = 30

III

**2**

- Check whether pupils can apply the three strategies to subtract a 1-digit number from a 2-digit number without regrouping:
  - 'Counting back' method
  - Vertical subtraction with place value chart
  - Using number bonds

**3**

**a**

- Ask pupils to work on this problem.
  **Step 1**: Counting back in tens: 70, …, 20, …10.
  **Step 2**: Counting on in ones. Encourage pupils to say and practise the strategy.

**b**

- Explain the vertical subtraction strategy using a place value chart. Notice that no regrouping is needed in this section. Model and explain the following strategy using vertical subtraction:
  **Step 1**: Subtract the ones. Write the result in the ones column.
  **Step 2**: Subtract the tens. 4 tens from 40 is subtracted from 7 tens from 70. Write the result under the tens column. The result is 3 tens which is 30.

Additional activity

Ask pupils to work in pairs.

Pupil A calls out a 2-digit number less than 100 and a 1-digit number which is less than the ones of the 2-digit number. Pupil B subtracts the smaller number from the larger number using any of the 3 subtraction methods given in **1**.

Pupils A and B swap roles.

## Additional activity

Ask pupils to work in pairs.

Pupil A calls out a 2-digit number less than 100 and a tens number.
Pupil B subtracts the smaller number from the larger number.
Pupils A and B swap roles.

## Teaching sequence

- Explain the vertical subtraction strategy using a place value chart. Notice that no regrouping is needed in this section. Model and explain the following strategy using vertical subtraction:

**Step 1**: Subtract the ones.
0 ones subtracted from 5 ones is 5 ones.
Write the result in the ones column.

**Step 2**: Subtract the tens.
3 tens from 30 is subtracted from 8 tens from 85.
The result is 5 tens.
Write the result in the tens column.
The result is 5 tens and 5 ones which is 55.

- Ask pupils to recall number bonds and use the strategy to subtract the corresponding tens and ones.

---

### Unit 17 Numbers to 100

 85 – 30 = ?

Use a place value chart.

85 = 8 tens 5 ones
30 = 3 tens 0 ones

| Tens | Ones |
|------|------|
| 85 | |

First subtract the ones.

```
  Tens   Ones
    8      5
 -  3      0
 _____
           5
```

5 ones – 0 ones = 5 ones

| Tens | Ones |
|------|------|
| 55 | |

Then subtract the tens.

```
  Tens   Ones
    8      5
 -  3      0
 _____
    5      5
```

8 tens – 3 tens = 5 tens

85 – 30 = 55

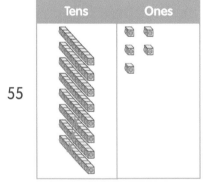

85 – 30
5 – 0 = 5
80 – 30 = 50

112

## Additional activity

Ask pupils to work in pairs.

Pupil A calls out two 2-digit numbers less than 100. The ones of the second number should not be greater than the first number. Pupil B subtracts the smaller number from the larger number using any of the 3 subtraction methods given in ❶.

Pupils A and B swap roles.

---

**5** Subtract the numbers.

**a**

| Tens | Ones |
|------|------|
| 7 | 2 |
| − 4 | 0 |

3 2

First subtract the ones.

2 ones − 0 ones = 2 ones

Then subtract the tens.

7 tens − 4 tens = 3 tens

**b** 96 − 20 = 76

**c** 68 − 50 = 18

**6** 58 − 24 = ?

Use a place value chart.

58 = 5 tens 8 ones
24 = 2 tens 4 ones

| Tens | Ones |
|------|------|
| 58 | |

First subtract the ones.

| Tens | Ones |
|------|------|
| 5 | 8 |
| − 2 | 4 |
| | 4 |

8 ones − 4 ones = 4 ones

| Tens | Ones |
|------|------|
| 34 | |

Then subtract the tens.

| Tens | Ones |
|------|------|
| 5 | 8 |
| − 2 | 4 |
| 3 | 4 |

5 tens − 2 tens = 3 tens

58 − 24 = 34

113

---

## Teaching sequence

**5**

- Check whether pupils can apply the vertical subtraction strategy or using the number bond method to subtract tens from a 2-digit number without regrouping.
- Explain to pupils that they may use any of the above strategies to solve the problem.

**6**

- Explain the vertical subtraction strategy using a place value chart. Notice that no regrouping is needed in this section. Model and explain the following strategy using vertical subtraction:

  **Step 1**: Subtract the ones. 4 ones subtracted from 8 ones is 4 ones. Write the result in the ones column.

  **Step 2**: Subtract the tens. 2 tens from 24 is subtracted from 5 tens from 58. The result is 3 tens. Write the result in the tens column. The result is 3 tens and 4 ones which is 34.

- Ask pupils to recall number bonds and use the strategy to subtract the corresponding tens and ones.

Ask pupils to work in pairs.

Pupil A writes down two 2-digit numbers less than 100 in vertical form. The ones of the second number should not be greater than those of the first number. Pupil B subtracts the smaller number from the larger number using any of the 2 subtraction methods given in **5** and **7**

Pupils A and B swap roles.

**Independent work**

Practice 7 in Practice Book ID, pp 59 to 62.

## Teaching sequence

- Check whether pupils can apply the vertical subtraction strategy or use the number bond method to subtract tens from a 2-digit number without regrouping.
- Explain to pupils that they can use any of these strategies to solve the problem.

---

**Unit 17** Numbers to 100

**7** Subtract the numbers.

**a**

| Tens | Ones |
|------|------|
| 6 | 9 |
| − 3 | 3 |
| 3 | 6 |

First subtract the ones.

9 ones − 3 ones = 6 ones

Then subtract the tens.

6 tens − 3 tens = 3 tens

**b**

| Tens | Ones |
|------|------|
| 7 | 5 |
| − 2 | 2 |
| 5 | 3 |

First subtract the ones.

5 ones − 2 ones = 3 ones

Then subtract the tens.

7 tens − 2 tens = 5 tens

**c**

```
    9   6
  − 4   1
  ─────────
    5   5
  ─────────
```

**d**

```
    8   9
  − 5   7
  ─────────
    3   2
  ─────────
```

Practice Book ID, p.59

114

## Learning objectives:
## More subtraction

**Pupils will be able to:**

- subtract a 1-digit number from a 2-digit number with regrouping
- subtract a 2-digit number from another 2-digit number with regrouping
- apply the regrouping concept in subtraction
- use the number bond strategy to subtract

## Key concept

The 'taking away' concept is used in subtraction.

## Thinking skill

Analysing parts and whole

## What you will need

Base ten equipment

---

Numbers to 100 **Unit 17**

# Let's Learn!

 More subtraction

**1** 52 – 9 = ?

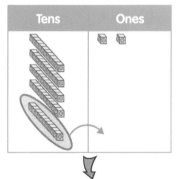

52

43

52 – 9 = 43

> First subtract the ones.
> We can't subtract
> 9 ones from 2 ones.
> Instead we regroup the
> tens and ones in 52.

Regroup the tens in 52.
52 = 5 tens 2 ones
   = 4 tens 12 ones

First subtract the ones.

12 ones – 9 ones = 3 ones

Then subtract the tens.

4 tens – 0 tens = 4 tens

115

## Teaching sequence

**1**

- Explain and revise regrouping in subtraction.
- Assess pupils using the examples below to gauge if they are able to carry out regrouping from tens to ones, as this is an essential skill in this section:

  73 = 7 tens 3 ones
     = 6 tens _____ ones
  65 = 5 tens _____ ones

- Use base ten equipment for support.
- Show with concrete representation how to regroup 52 to 4 tens and 12 ones.
- Introduce and explain the vertical subtraction strategy using a place value chart.
- Notice that regrouping is needed in this section. Model and explain the following strategy using vertical subtraction:

  **Step 1**: Subtract the ones. Show the regrouping process then subtract vertically:
  12 ones – 9 ones = 3 ones
  Write the result in the ones column.

  **Step 2**: Subtract the tens.
  4 tens – 0 tens = 4 tens
  Write the result in the tens column.
  The result is 4 tens and 3 ones which is 43.

Ask pupils to work in pairs.

Pupil A writes down two 2-digit numbers less than 100 vertically. The ones of the second number should be greater than those of the first number. Pupil B subtracts the smaller number from the larger number using any of the subtraction methods given in  and **2**.

Pupils A and B swap roles.

## Teaching sequence

**2**

- Explain the subtraction procedure using the strategy shown in .
- Emphasise the regrouping procedure using concrete representation:

  74 = 6 tens 14 ones
- Show the regrouping of 74 into 6 tens and 14 ones with concrete representation.
- Introduce and explain the vertical subtraction strategy using a place value chart. Notice that regrouping is needed in this section. Model and explain the following strategy using vertical subtraction:

  **Step 1**: Subtract the ones. Show regrouping process then subtract vertically:

  14 ones – 8 ones = 6 ones
  Write the result in the ones column.

  **Step 2**: Subtract the tens.
  6 tens – 3 tens = 3 tens
  Write the result under the tens column.
  The result is 3 tens and 6 ones which is 36.

---

**Unit 17** Numbers to 100

**2** 74 – 38 = ?

74

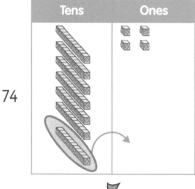

First subtract the ones. We can't subtract 8 ones from 4 ones. Instead we regroup the tens and ones in 74.

Regroup the tens in 74.
74 = 7 tens 4 ones
   = 6 tens 14 ones

First subtract the ones.

$$
\begin{array}{cc}
\text{Tens} & \text{Ones} \\
{}^6\cancel{7} & {}^1 4 \\
-\ 3 & 8 \\
\hline
 & 6 \\
\end{array}
$$

14 ones – 8 ones = 6 ones

36

Then subtract the tens.

$$
\begin{array}{cc}
\text{Tens} & \text{Ones} \\
{}^6\cancel{7} & {}^1 4 \\
-\ 3 & 8 \\
\hline
3 & 6 \\
\end{array}
$$

6 tens – 3 tens = 3 tens

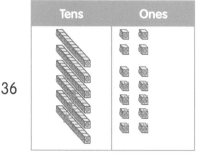

116

74 – 38 = 36

**3** Regroup and subtract the numbers.

| Tens | Ones |
|------|------|
| 5 | 5 |
| – | 7 |

4  8

Regroup the tens and ones in 55.

55 = 5 tens [ 5 ] ones

= 4 tens [ 15 ] ones

First subtract the ones.

[ 15 ] ones – [ 7 ] ones = [ 8 ] ones

Then subtract the tens.

[ 4 ] tens – [ 0 ] tens = [ 4 ] tens

**4** Subtract the numbers.

| Tens | Ones |
|------|------|
| 7 | 0 |
| – 5 | 5 |

1  5

Regroup the tens and ones in 70.

70 = 7 tens [ 0 ] ones

= 6 tens [ 10 ] ones

First subtract the ones.

[ 10 ] ones – [ 5 ] ones = [ 5 ] ones

Then subtract the tens.

[ 6 ] tens – [ 5 ] tens = [ 1 ] ten

**5**
| 7 | 4 |
|---|---|
| – |  9 |

6  5

**6**
| 6 | 2 |
|---|---|
| – 5 | 8 |

4

117

**3**

- Check whether pupils can use vertical subtraction to subtract a 1-digit number from a 2-digit number by regrouping. Reinforce the regrouping concept using this question.

**4**

- Check whether pupils can use vertical subtraction to subtract a 2-digit number from another 2-digit number by regrouping. Reinforce the regrouping concept using this question.

**5** and **6**

- Ask pupils to practise using these questions.

## What you will need
- I counter for each player
- I dice for each group

## Teaching sequence

**7** *Game*
- Ask pupils to work in small groups.
- Model how to play the game.
- Ask them to write down their points as they move along the board.

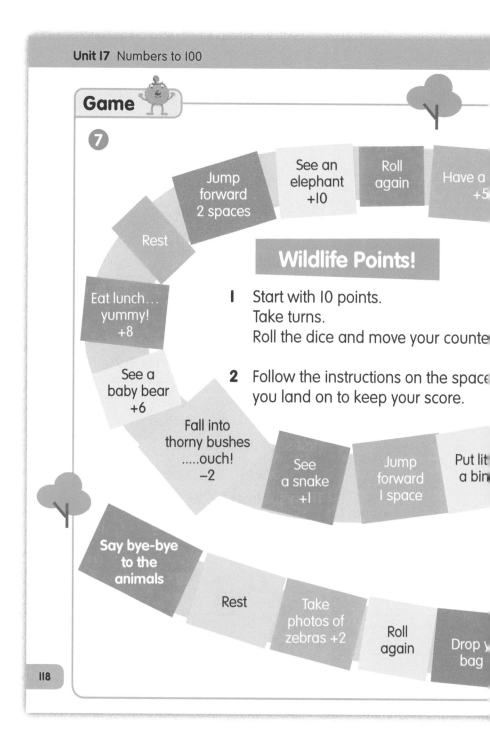

**Game**

**7**

Jump forward 2 spaces

See an elephant +10

Roll again

Have a
+5

Rest

## Wildlife Points!

1  Start with 10 points.
   Take turns.
   Roll the dice and move your counte

Eat lunch... yummy! +8

See a baby bear +6

2  Follow the instructions on the space
   you land on to keep your score.

Fall into thorny bushes .....ouch! −2

See a snake +1

Jump forward I space

Put lit a bin

Say bye-bye to the animals

Rest

Take photos of zebras +2

Roll again

Drop y bag

118

## Independent work

Practice 8 and Practice 9 in
Practice Book ID, pp 63 to 68.

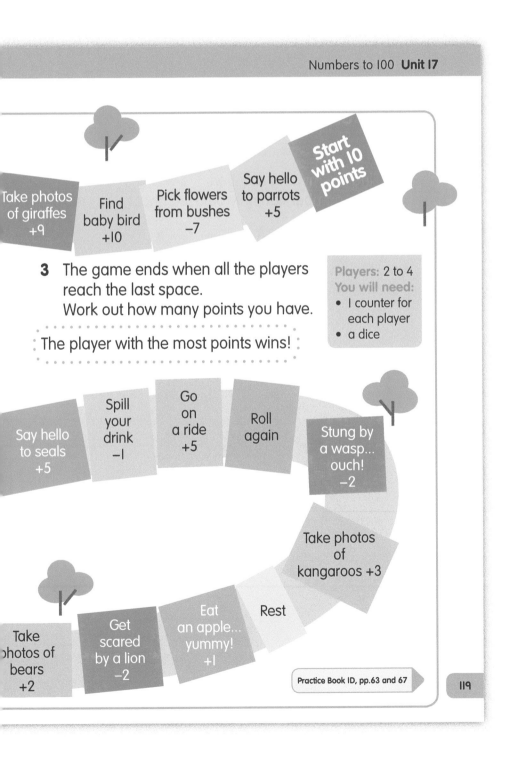

Take photos of giraffes +9

Find baby bird +10

Pick flowers from bushes −7

Say hello to parrots +5

**Start with 10 points**

**3** The game ends when all the players reach the last space.
Work out how many points you have.

The player with the most points wins!

**Players:** 2 to 4
**You will need:**
- 1 counter for each player
- a dice

Say hello to seals +5

Spill your drink −1

Go on a ride +5

Roll again

Stung by a wasp... ouch! −2

Take photos of kangaroos +3

Take photos of bears +2

Get scared by a lion −2

Eat an apple... yummy! +1

Rest

Practice Book ID, pp.63 and 67

119

## Thinking skills

- Deduction
- Identifying patterns and relationships

## Heuristics for problem solving

- Simplify the problem
- Guess and check

## Objective of activity

Pupils will be able to use the number bond strategy to connect numbers to make addition and subtraction sentences up to 100.

## Independent work

*Challenging Practice* and *Problem Solving* in Practice Book ID, pp 69 to 70.

## Teaching sequence

⑧ *Put On Your Thinking Caps!*

- The strategy is to think of 2 number bonds in addition. Encourage pupils to follow these steps:
- First simplify the problem by checking the ones of the 2-digit numbers. The sum of two of them should give the third one.

  E.g. These are two sets of addition sentences:

  4 + 5 = 9

  9 + 5 = 14

- Next try a greater number. By guessing and checking, pupils should find these answers:

  25 + 49 = 74

  25 + 14 = 39

  The common number is 25, which would be at the top of the tree.

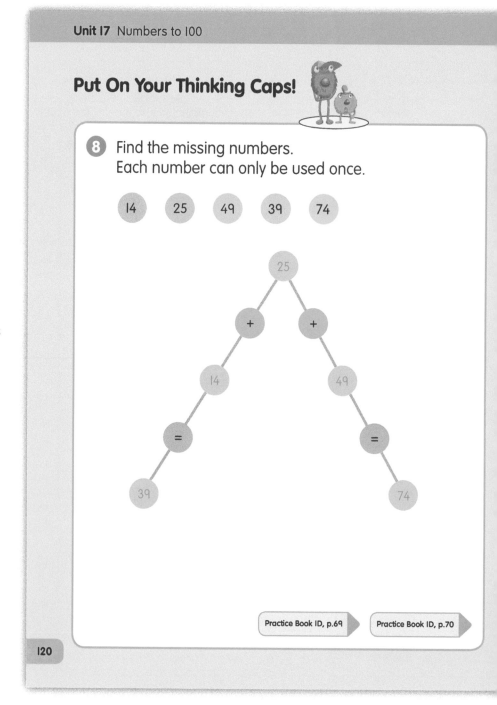

**Put On Your Thinking Caps!**

⑧ Find the missing numbers.
Each number can only be used once.

14    25    49    39    74

25

+    +

14    49

=    =

39    74

Practice Book ID, p.69    Practice Book ID, p.70

120

**Practice 1** Counting

1 Count in tens and ones.
Fill in the spaces.

Example

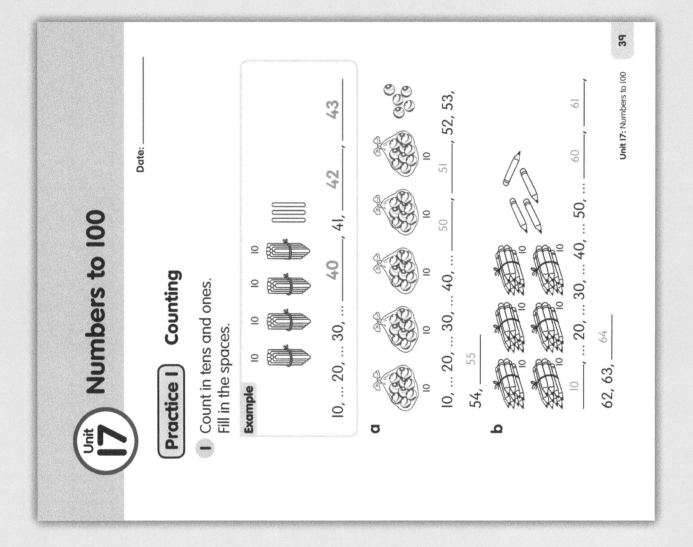

10, ... 20, ... 30, ... _40_, 41, _42_, _43_

**a**

10, ... 20, ... 30, ... 40, ... _____, _50_, _51_, _52, 53, _____

54, _55_

**b**

_10_, ... 20, ... 30, ... 40, ... 50, ... _60_, _61_, _____

62, 63, _64_

**2** Write the numbers.

a forty-nine _49_

b sixty-eight _68_

c ninety-five _95_

d eighty-seven _87_

e fifty-six _56_

f seventy-three _73_

**3** Write the numbers in words.

a 40 _forty_

b 51 _fifty-one_

c 72 _seventy-two_

d 88 _eighty-eight_

**4** Find the missing numbers.

a 60 and 4 make _64_.

b 5 and 70 make _75_.

c 50 and _3_ make 53.

d _80_ and 4 make 84.

Date: _____

**Practice 2** Place value

**1** Look at the pictures.
Then fill in the spaces.

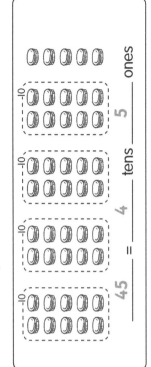

45 = _4_ tens _5_ ones

a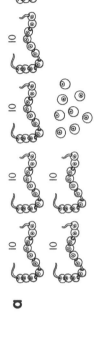

78 = _7_ tens _8_ ones

b

36 = _3_ tens _6_ ones

**2** Look at the pictures.
Then fill in the spaces.

**a**

69 = 6 tens 9 ones

60 + 9 = 69

**b**

93 = 9 tens 3 ones

90 + 3 = 93

**c**

87 = 8 tens 7 ones

80 + 7 = 87

**c**

92 = 9 tens 2 ones

**d**

57 = 5 tens 7 ones

**e**

84 = 8 tens 4 ones

## Practice 3　Comparing, order and pattern

**1 a** Which set has more stars?
Group the numbers in tens.
Then compare the difference.

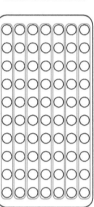

Set A　　　Set B

60 is 5 more than 55.
Set __B__ has more.

**b** Which set has fewer circles?
Group the circles in tens.
Then compare the difference.

Set A　　　Set B

70 is 5 more than 65.
Set __B__ has fewer.

---

**3** Fill in the place value charts.

**a** 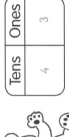 43

| Tens | Ones |
|---|---|
| 4 | 3 |

**b** 86

| Tens | Ones |
|---|---|
| 8 | 6 |

**c** 64

| Tens | Ones |
|---|---|
| 6 | 4 |

**d** 97

| Tens | Ones |
|---|---|
| 9 | 7 |

**e** 75

| Tens | Ones |
|---|---|
| 7 | 5 |

**2** Which number is greater? Circle it.

Example | 50 or (71)

a 72 or (87)

b (92) or 69

c (54) or 45

d 67 or (76)

e (86) or 83

f 94 or (98)

**3** Which number is smaller? Circle it.

Example | (62) or 81

a (59) or 71

b (68) or 93

c (79) or 97

d 84 or (48)

e (62) or 67

f 96 or (91)

---

**4** Compare the numbers.
Then fill in the spaces.

a

65  72  49

The smallest number is _49_.

The greatest number is _72_.

b

73  69  90

The smallest number is _69_.

The greatest number is _90_.

c

54  45  88  99

The smallest number is _45_.

The greatest number is _99_.

## Practice 4  Simple addition

1 Add the numbers by counting on.

**Example**

73, 74, 75, 76, 77

73 + 4 = 77

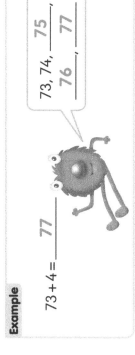

a  85 + 3 = 88

85, 86, 87, 88

b  62 + 6 = 68

62, 63, 64, 65, 66, 67, 68

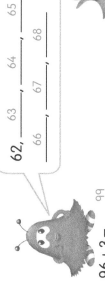

c  96 + 3 = 99

96, 97, 98, 99

---

5 Use the numbers to fill in the spaces.

| 92 | 67 | 84 | 100 | 73 | 46 |

The greatest number is 100.

The smallest number is 46.

46, 67 and 73 are less than 84.

92 and 100 are greater than 84.

67 is greater than 46 but less than 100.

92 is less than 100 but greater than 50.

6 The numbers are arranged in a pattern. Find the missing numbers.

a  50, 51, 52, 53, 54, 55, 56, 57, 58

b  73, 72, 71, 70, 69, 68, 67

c  85, 87, 89, 91, 93, 95

d  99, 97, 95, 93, 91, 89

e  50, 60, 70, 80, 90, 100

f  93, 83, 73, 63, 53, 43, 33

## 2 Add the numbers.

**a**

| | | |
|---|---|---|
| | 5 | 3 |
| + | | 4 |
| | 5 | 7 |

**b**

| | | |
|---|---|---|
| | 6 | 2 |
| + | | 7 |
| | 6 | 9 |

**c**

| | | |
|---|---|---|
| | 8 | 3 |
| + | | 5 |
| | 8 | 8 |

**d**

| | | |
|---|---|---|
| | 4 | 4 |
| + | | 5 |
| | 4 | 9 |

**e**

| | | |
|---|---|---|
| | | 2 |
| + | 6 | 3 |
| | 6 | 5 |

**f**

| | | |
|---|---|---|
| | | 4 |
| + | 7 | 3 |
| | 7 | 7 |

**g** 5 + 82 = 87

| | | |
|---|---|---|
| | | 5 |
| + | 8 | 2 |
| | 8 | 7 |

**h** 93 + 2 = 95

| | | |
|---|---|---|
| | 9 | 3 |
| + | | 2 |
| | 9 | 5 |



## 3 Add the numbers.

**a**

| | | |
|---|---|---|
| | 4 | 0 |
| + | 5 | 0 |
| | 9 | 0 |

**b**

| | | |
|---|---|---|
| | 6 | 0 |
| + | 2 | 3 |
| | 8 | 3 |

**c**

| | | |
|---|---|---|
| | 3 | 7 |
| + | 4 | 0 |
| | 7 | 7 |

**d**

| | | |
|---|---|---|
| | 5 | 3 |
| + | 4 | 5 |
| | 9 | 8 |

**e**

| | | |
|---|---|---|
| | 6 | 3 |
| + | 2 | 4 |
| | 8 | 7 |

**f**

| | | |
|---|---|---|
| | 4 | 7 |
| + | 1 | 2 |
| | 5 | 9 |

**g** 56 + 23 = 79

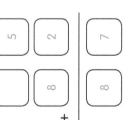

| | | |
|---|---|---|
| | 5 | 6 |
| + | 2 | 3 |
| | 7 | 9 |

**h** 86 + 13 = 99

| | | |
|---|---|---|
| | 8 | 6 |
| + | 1 | 3 |
| | 9 | 9 |

## Practice 5 | More addition

1 Add the numbers.

a
```
   4 8
 +   5
 ─────
   5 3
```

b
```
   5 7
 +   8
 ─────
   6 5
```

c
```
   6 7
 +   4
 ─────
   7 1
```

d
```
   5 9
 +   4
 ─────
   6 3
```

e
```
   7 3
 +   9
 ─────
   8 2
```

f
```
   8 5
 +   6
 ─────
   9 1
```

g  $7 + 66 =$ 73

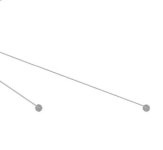

```
   6 6
 +   7
 ─────
   7 3
```

h  $89 + 8 =$ 97

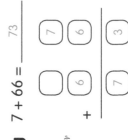

```
   8 9
 +   8
 ─────
   9 7
```

---

4 Match each cake to the correct child.

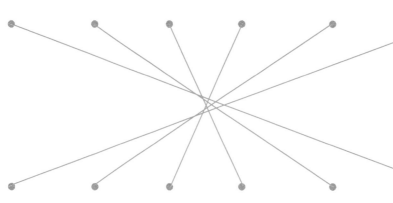

20 + 70 → 90
0 + 42 → 42
22 + 71 → 93
72 + 5 → 77
54 + 31 → 85
40 + 49 → 89

  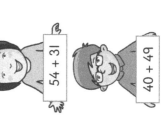      

Cakes: 89  85  77  93  42  90

**3** Add and regroup.
Fill in the missing numbers.

a
```
   2 7
 + 2 8
 -----
   5 5
```

b
```
   8 6
 + 1 4
 -----
 1 0 0
```

c
```
   2 5
 + 3 7
 -----
   6 2
```

d
```
   4 4
 + 3 7
 -----
   8 1
```

e
```
   3 9
 + 2 1
 -----
   6 0
```

f
```
   3 6
 + 5 4
 -----
   9 0
```

g  19 + 14 = 33

| [1] | [9] |
| [1] | [4] |
| + | |
| [3] | [3] |

h  58 + 36 = 94

| [5] | [8] |
| [3] | [6] |
| + | |
| [9] | [4] |

---

**2** Jack drops a ball into the number machine below.
What happens to the number on the ball?
Write the answer in the ◯.

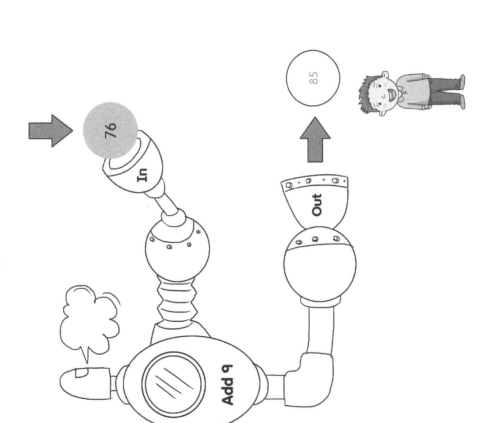

In 76

Add 9

Out 85

Date: _____

## Practice 6   More addition

1 Miya drops a ball into the number machine.
Which number is on the ball?
Write the number in the ◯.

31    39    29

In    29

Add 69

Out

98

---

4 Add the numbers.

| | | |
|---|---|---|
| 52 + 19 = 71 | 58 + 6 = 64 | 67 + 18 = 85 |
| 48 + 38 = 86 | 7 + 59 = 66 | 43 + 57 = 100 |
| 27 + 49 = 76 | 18 + 67 = 85 | 56 + 35 = 91 |

## Practice 7 | Simple subtraction

1 Count back to subtract the numbers.

**Example**

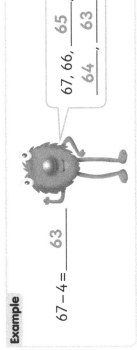

67 − 4 = **63**

67, 66, **65** , **64** , **63**

a 95 − 3 = _____ 92

95, 94, 93 , _____ , 92

b 88 − 5 = _____ 83

88, 87, 86 , 85

84 , 83

c 79 − 6 = _____ 73

79, 78, 77 , 76

75 , 74 , 73

2 Find the answer to the joke.

**What fish do you find in space?**

a 45 + 7 = **52** T

b 52 + 5 = _____ A 57

c 2 + 78 = _____ S 80

d 72 + 8 = _____ S 80

e 2 + 70 = _____ R 72

f 64 + 19 = _____ I 83

g 28 + 40 = _____ H 68

h 61 + 16 = _____ F 77

| S | T | A | R | F | I | S | H |
|----|----|----|----|----|----|----|----|
| 80 | 52 | 57 | 72 | 77 | 83 | 80 | 68 |

## 3 Subtract the numbers.

**a**
```
   9 5
 - 2 0
 -----
   7 5
```

**b**
```
   6 9
 - 3 0
 -----
   3 9
```

**c**
```
   7 0
 - 2 0
 -----
   5 0
```

**d**
```
   4 0
 - 2 0
 -----
   2 0
```

**e**
```
   6 8
 - 3 2
 -----
   3 6
```

**f**
```
   9 7
 - 5 4
 -----
   4 3
```

**g** 56 – 23 = 33

| 5 | 6 |
|---|---|
| 2 | 3 |
| 3 | 3 |

**h** 86 – 42 = 44

| 8 | 6 |
|---|---|
| 4 | 2 |
| 4 | 4 |

---

## 2 Subtract the numbers.

**a**
```
   5 8
 -   3
 -----
   5 5
```

**b**
```
   6 9
 -   4
 -----
   6 5
```

**c**
```
   7 8
 -   3
 -----
   7 5
```

**d**
```
   6 7
 -   5
 -----
   6 2
```

**e**
```
   9 6
 -   3
 -----
   9 3
```

**f**
```
   8 8
 -   7
 -----
   8 1
```

**g** 79 – 6 = 73

| 7 | 9 |
|---|---|
|   | 6 |
| 7 | 3 |

**h** 99 – 5 = 94

| 9 | 9 |
|---|---|
|   | 5 |
| 9 | 4 |

## Practice 8  More subtraction

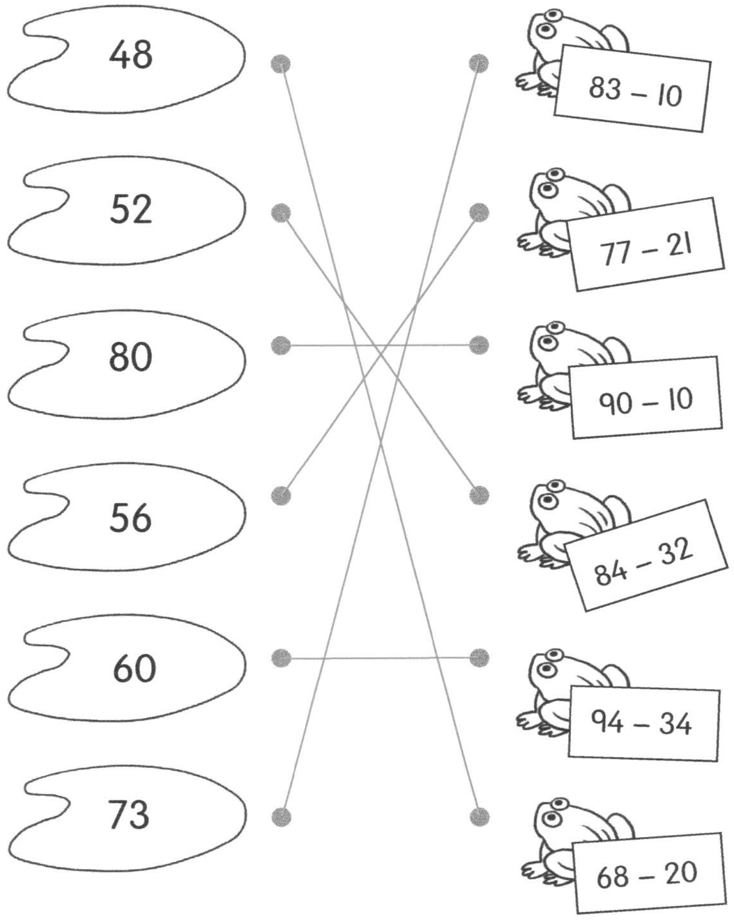

1  Subtract the numbers.

a
```
  6 4
-   8
-----
  5 6
```

b
```
  9 3
-   5
-----
  8 8
```

c
```
  7 8
-   9
-----
  6 9
```

d
```
  8 7
-   8
-----
  7 9
```

e
```
  5 0
-   2
-----
  4 8
```

f
```
  8 0
-   6
-----
  7 4
```

g  72 − 9 = 63

h  91 − 4 = 87

4  Match.

48    83 – 10
52    77 – 21
80    90 – 10
56    84 – 32
60    94 – 34
73    68 – 20

**3** Regroup and subtract the numbers.

a)
$$\begin{array}{r} 5\ 2 \\ -\ 3\ 8 \\ \hline 1\ 4 \end{array}$$

b)
$$\begin{array}{r} 7\ 6 \\ -\ 4\ 9 \\ \hline 2\ 7 \end{array}$$

c)
$$\begin{array}{r} 8\ 5 \\ -\ 3\ 8 \\ \hline 4\ 7 \end{array}$$

d)
$$\begin{array}{r} 5\ 3 \\ -\ 4\ 7 \\ \hline 6 \end{array}$$

e)
$$\begin{array}{r} 9\ 0 \\ -\ 5\ 6 \\ \hline 3\ 4 \end{array}$$

f)
$$\begin{array}{r} 7\ 3 \\ -\ 5\ 6 \\ \hline 1\ 7 \end{array}$$

g) $83 - 26 = \underline{57}$

| 8 | 3 |
|---|---|
| 2 | 6 |

$$\begin{array}{r} 5\ 7 \end{array}$$

h) $95 - 38 = \underline{57}$

| 9 | 5 |
|---|---|
| 3 | 8 |

$$\begin{array}{r} 5\ 7 \end{array}$$

**2** Tai drops a ball into the number machine.
Which number is on the ball?
Write the number in the ◯.

 85

 69

 75

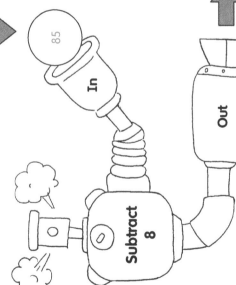

In 85

Subtract 8

Out

77

## Practice 9  More subtraction

1. Find the answer to each subtraction sentence.
   Then colour the circle with the correct answer.

| 53 – 19 | ••••• |
| 73 – 30 | ••••• |
| 81 – 46 | ••••• |
| 60 – 27 | ••••• |
| 70 – 30 | ••••• |
| 94 – 74 | ••••• |
| 90 – 5 | ••••• |

Circles: 54   84   34
43   56
34   35   45
43   33   47
40   33   63
21   20   29
85   53   67

---

4. Ella drops a ball into the number machine.
   Which number is on the ball?
   Write the number in the ◯.

Balls: 90   64   54

In 90 → Subtract 43 → Out 47

**Answers  Unit 17:** Numbers to 100    **223**

## Challenging Practice

The Hundred Train is here!
On its coaches are two numbers which add up to 100.

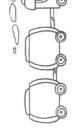

38 + 62 = 100

The numbers on its coaches add up to 100.
Write two numbers for each train below.

1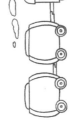

2

3

4

(Accept all possible answers.
Examples: 46 + 54 = 100,
81 + 19 = 100, 63 + 37 = 100)

---

**2** Subtract the numbers.

a  56 – 8 = ___48___

b  73 – 4 = ___69___

c  67 – 8 = ___59___

d  75 – 9 = ___66___

e  50 – 40 = ___10___

f  87 – 11 = ___76___

g  90 – 50 = ___40___

h  93 – 20 = ___73___

i  58 – 18 = ___40___

j  61 – 14 = ___47___

k  47 – 39 = ___8___

l  53 – 27 = ___26___

m  30 – 28 = ___2___

n  90 – 88 = ___2___

Date: _____

## Problem Solving

1   Millie has 8 stickers.
    She buys 3 more stickers every day.
    How many days will it take her to collect 17 stickers altogether?

I have 8 stickers.

Count on from 8.
8, ... 11, ... 14, ... 17
It will take 3 days for her to collect 17 stickers altogether.

# Unit 18: Money (1)

| Week | Learning Objectives | Thinking Skills | Resources |
|---|---|---|---|
| 6 | **(1) Getting to know our money**<br><br>Pupils will be able to:<br>• recognise and name different notes and coins<br>• know that p stands for pence and £ stands for pounds<br>• name the things they can buy using each coin/note<br>• recognise, count and write the number of coins and notes for each denomination | • Classifying<br>• Comparing | • Pupil Textbook 1B, pp 121 to 122<br>• Practice Book 1D, pp 71 to 74<br>• Teacher's Guide 1B, pp 229 to 230 |
| 6 | **(2) Exchanging money**<br><br>Pupils will be able to:<br>• match a coin of one denomination to an equivalent set of coins of another denomination<br>• match a note of one denomination to an equivalent set of coins or notes of another denomination | • Analysing parts and whole | • Pupil Textbook 1B, pp 123 to 124<br>• Practice Book 1D, pp 75 to 78<br>• Teacher's Guide 1B, pp 231 to 232 |

# Unit 18: Money (I)

Medium-term plan

| Week | Learning Objectives | Thinking Skills | Resources |
|------|---------------------|-----------------|-----------|
| 6 | *Let's Explore!*<br><br>Pupils will be able to:<br>• exchange a £2 coin for other coins<br>• write down the different ways of exchanging 10p, 20p, £1, £2, £5 for other coins<br>• write down the different ways of exchanging 100p and think of the smallest number of coins | • Analysing parts and whole | • Pupil Textbook 1B, pp 125 to 126<br>• Teacher's Guide 1B, pp 233 to 234 |
| 6 | **(3) Work out the amount of money**<br><br>Pupils will be able to:<br>• count the amount of money in pence (up to £1) using the 'counting on' strategy<br>• count the amount of money in pounds (up to £100) using the 'counting on' strategy<br>• think of whether to pay with a £2 coin or a £1 coin when buying different items<br>• choose the correct value of coins for purchasing items | • Analysing parts and whole | • Pupil Textbook 1B, pp 127 to 131<br>• Practice Book 1D, pp 79 to 84<br>• Teacher's Guide 1B, pp 235 to 239 |

# Unit 18: Money (I)

Medium-term plan

| Week | Learning Objectives | Thinking Skills | Resources |
|---|---|---|---|
| | *Maths Journal* <br><br> Pupils will be able to: <br> • calculate and select the correct statements that match <br> • calculate the amount in notes and coins | | |
| 7 | *Put On Your Thinking Caps!* <br><br> Pupils will be able to: <br> • guess and check the notes under a cup that add up to £50 <br> • make a systematic list of the different ways to get £50 | • Analysing parts and whole <br> • Induction <br><br> Heuristic for problem solving: <br> • Making a systematic list | • Pupil Textbook IB, p 131 <br> • Practice Book ID, pp 85 to 88 <br> • Teacher's Guide IB p 239 |

# Money (I)

**Learning objectives:**
## Getting to know our money

**Pupils will be able to:**

- recognise and name different notes and coins
- know that p stands for pence and £ stands for pounds
- name the things they can buy using each coin/note

- recognise, count and write the number of coins and notes for each denomination

## Key concept

Coins and notes in pounds and pence can be used to pay for goods and services.

## Thinking skills

- Classifying
- Comparing

## What you will need

- Several coins and notes of different denominations
- Play money (see Photocopy master 7 on page 290)

---

### Unit 18 Money (I)

**Let's Learn!**

### Getting to know our money

**❶**

1p coin   2p coin   5p coin   10p coin   20p coin   50p coin   £1 coin   £2 coin

**What can you buy with each coin?** Answers vary

**❷**

£5 note    £10 note    £20 note

£50 note

p means **pence**!
£ means **pounds**!

**What can you buy with each note?** Answers vary

121

## Teaching sequence

**❶**

- Discuss with pupils what 'money' means. Explain why we need money, and give examples of situations where money is used.
- Point out the coins of different denominations. Show each coin one at a time and encourage pupils to recognise and name the coin.
- Discuss the value of the different coins. See if pupils are able to distinguish the coins worth pounds from the coins worth pence. Explain that one hundred pennies, or pence, makes up one pound. Show the symbols we use to represent pence (p) and pounds (£).
- Discuss with the class what they can buy with each coin.

**❷**

- Point out the notes of different denominations. Show each note one at a time and encourage pupils to recognise and name the note.
- Discuss the value of the different notes. Use the pound sign to show how we record the value of each note in symbols.
- Discuss with the class what they can buy with each note.

## Thinking skill

Classifying

## What you will need

Play money for each group in notes and coins as shown (see Photocopy master 7 on page 290)

## Additional activities

- Encourage pupils to look at both sides of coins and notes of different denominations, and ask them to describe the size, colour and images on each side.
- Ask pupils to work in groups of four. Distribute notes and coins of different denominations to each group. Call out the name of a coin or note, and ask pupils to select and show the correct coin or note.

## Independent work

Practice I in Practice Book ID, pp 71 to 74.

## Teaching sequence

- Give pupils the notes and coins shown in the textbook.
- Ask pupils to work in groups to sort the money according to the different denominations and record the number of each type of coin and note.
- Alternatively, you can ask pupils to look at the picture in the textbook.
- Encourage the groups to discuss their answers.
- Ask the groups:
  - Which coin do you see the most?
  - Which note do you see the most?
  - How many more 5p coins than Ip coins are there?
  - How many notes are there altogether?

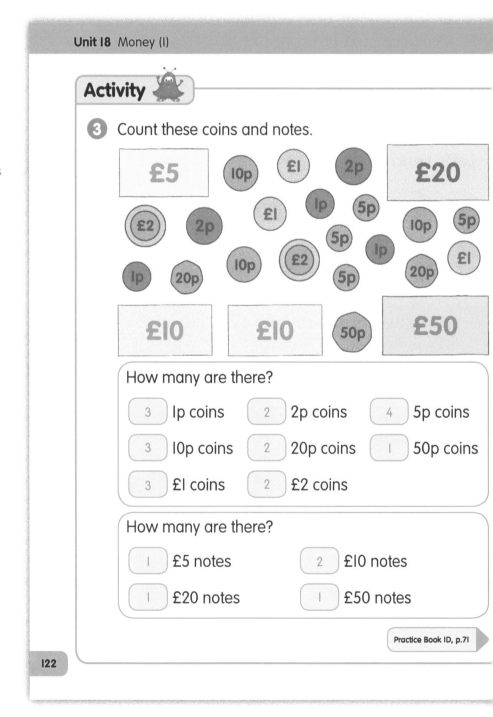

Unit 18  Money (I)

**Activity**

3 Count these coins and notes.

£5   10p   £1   2p   £20

£2   2p   £1   Ip   5p   10p   5p

5p   Ip   £1

Ip   20p   10p   £2   5p   20p

£10   £10   50p   £50

How many are there?

| 3 | Ip coins | 2 | 2p coins | 4 | 5p coins |
| 3 | 10p coins | 2 | 20p coins | I | 50p coins |
| 3 | £1 coins | 2 | £2 coins | | |

How many are there?

| I | £5 notes | 2 | £10 notes |
| I | £20 notes | I | £50 notes |

Practice Book ID, p.71

122

## Learning objectives: Exchanging money

**Pupils will be able to:**

- match a coin of one denomination to an equivalent set of coins of another denomination
- match a note of one denomination to an equivalent set of coins or notes of another denomination

## Key concept

A coin or note of one denomination can be used as the equivalent of another set of coins or notes of a smaller denomination.

## Thinking skill

Analysing parts and whole

## What you will need

Play money in notes and coins of different denominations (see Photocopy master 7 on page 290)

---

# Let's Learn!

### Exchanging money

**1** We can exchange coins.

| one 2p coin | 2p = 1p 1p | two 1p coins |
| one 5p coin | 5p = 1p 1p 1p 1p 1p | five 1p coins |
| one 10p coin | 10p = 5p 5p | two 5p coins |
| one 20p coin | 20p = 10p 10p | two 10p coins |
| one 50p coin | 50p = 10p 10p 10p 10p 10p | five 10p coins |
| one £1 coin | £1 = 10p 10p 10p 10p 10p 10p 10p 10p 10p 10p | ten 10p coins |

123

## Teaching sequence

**1**

- Discuss situations where pupils may need to exchange coins of one denomination for those of another denomination.

  E.g. A game machine only takes 50p coins. If you only have a £1 coin, you will need to change the coin to smaller denominations of two 50p coins.

- Exchange each coin for coins of smaller denominations.

  E.g. Exchange a 2p coin for two 1p coins; exchange a 20p coin for two 10p coins or twenty 1p coins.

- Work through the examples in the textbook together.

- Ask pupils to find other ways to exchange these coins for sets of smaller denominations.

Practice 2 in Practice Book ID,
pp 75 to 78.

## Teaching sequence

- Discuss situations where pupils may need to exchange notes of one denomination for notes or coins of another denomination.
- Show examples of how to exchange each note for notes or coins of smaller denominations.

  E.g. Exchange a £50 note for five £10 notes; exchange a £20 note for two £10 notes or four £5 notes.

- Work through the examples together.
- Ask pupils to find other ways to exchange these notes for sets of smaller denominations.

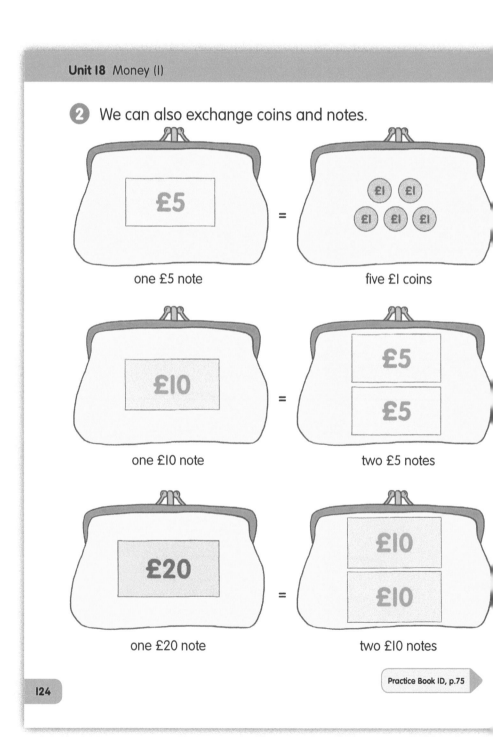

**Unit 18** Money (I)

**2** We can also exchange coins and notes.

one £5 note   =   five £1 coins

one £10 note   =   two £5 notes

one £20 note   =   two £10 notes

Practice Book ID, p.75

124

## Objectives of activity

Pupils will be able to:

- exchange a £2 coin for other coins
- write down the different ways of exchanging 10p, 20p, £1, £2, £5 for other coins
- write down the different ways of exchanging 100p and think of the smallest number of coins

## Thinking skill

Analysing parts and whole

## What you will need

Play money in notes and coins of different denominations (see Photocopy master 7 on page 290)

---

Money (I)  **Unit 18**

## Let's Explore!

**3**  **a**  Miya has a £2 coin.

She wants to exchange it for other coins.

What coins can she exchange it for?

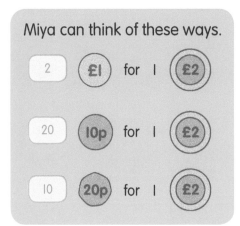

Write down other ways of exchanging the £2 coin.

*Answers vary*

**b**  Peter has some coins.

Ruby has some coins and a £5 note.

She wants to exchange her money with Peter.

Use the chart on the next page to write down the coins that Peter can give Ruby.

125

---

## Teaching sequence

**3**  *Let's Explore!*

**a**

- Ask pupils to work in pairs or groups to discuss all possibilities. Provide them with money.
- Note that at this stage pupils are only expected to change notes and coins to coins of only one denomination.

**b**

- Ask pupils to work in two groups, one group to act as Ruby and the other as Peter.
- Invite a volunteer from the first group to present the coin or note as shown in the table. Then choose a volunteer from the second group to exchange the coin or note for a set of coins of equal value.
- Ask the group to swap roles and repeat the activity above.

## Teaching sequence

- Ask pupils to complete the table. Note that exchanging should be to only one denomination.

c

- Ask pupils to work in small groups to discuss the question and think of as many answers as possible.
- Invite volunteers to share their answers with the class.

## Learning objectives: Work out the amount of money

**Pupils will be able to:**

- count the amount of money in pence (up to £1) using the 'counting on' strategy
- count the amount of money in pounds (up to £100) using the 'counting on' strategy
- think of whether to pay with a £2 coin or a £1 coin when buying different items
- choose the correct value of coins for purchasing items

## Key concept

The amount of money can be counted in pence (up to £1) and pounds (up to £100).

## Thinking skill

Analysing parts and whole

## What you will need

Play money in notes and coins of different denominations (see Photocopy master 7 on page 290)

---

## Let's Learn!

### Work out the amount of money

**1** Count on to find how much Jack has.

> 50, … 70, … 80, … 85 pence

Jack has 85p.

**2** Jack's mum has some money. How much does she have?

| £50 |
| --- |

| £10 | £10 |
| --- | --- |
| £10 | £10 |

| £5 |  |

> 50, … 60, … 70, … 80, … 90, … 95, … 97 pounds

Jack's mum has £97.

127

---

## Teaching sequence

**1**

- Explain to pupils the strategy of counting on to work out the amount of money with a set of coins. Pupils are expected to count by 5 and by 10 pence to find the amount of money.
- Hold up a 20p coin and a 10p coin.
  Say: *"20, 30. I have 30 pence."*
- Hold up three 10p coins and one 50p coin.
  Say: *"50, 60, 70, 80. I have 80 pence."*
- Hold up two 20p coins and one 5p coin.
  Say: *"20, 40, 45. I have 45 pence."*
- Work through the example in the textbook together and ask pupils to count aloud.

**2**

- Explain to pupils the strategy of counting on to work out the amount of money with a set of notes and coins. Pupils are expected to count by 1, 5, 10, 20 or 50 to work out the amount of money.
- Hold up a £5 note and one £2 coin.
  Say: *"5, 6, 7, I have £7."*
- Hold up three £2 coins and one £10 note.
  Say: *"10, 12, 14, 16. I have £16."*
- Work through the example in the textbook together and ask pupils to count aloud.

## Additional activity

Ask pupils to work in pairs.

Pupil A chooses a number of paper notes or coins but no combinations of coins and notes. Pupil B works out the value of the coins or notes by counting.

Pupils A and B swap roles.

## Teaching sequence

- Look for pupils who can apply the 'counting on' strategy to use the correct amount of money to buy the items shown in the textbook.
- For the kite, pupils should be able to count on by 2 to get £4.
- For the apples, pupils should be able to count on by 50, 10 and 5 to get 70 pence.
- For the drum, pupils should be able to count on by 10 and 5 to get £35.

---

**Unit 18** Money (I)

**3** Hardeep goes shopping.

drum          apples          kite

He pays ( **£2** ) ( **£2** ) for the kite.

The kite costs £ [ 4 ].

He pays **5p** **10p** **5p** **50p** for the apples.

The apples cost [ 70 ] p.

He pays **£10** **£10** **£10** **£5** for the drum.

The drum costs £ [ 35 ].

128

## Additional activity

Ask pupils to work in pairs.

Pupil A calls out an item and cost of the item in pounds or pence only, e.g., 75p, £13 etc.
Pupil B works out combinations of coins or notes to pay for the item.

Pupils A and B swap roles.

**4** It's lunch time and Ella is hungry.
Help her work out how to pay for different food and drinks.

### Cafe

Sandwich: £3
Jacket potato: £4
Pizza: £6

Apple juice: 70p
Water: 65p
Lemonade: 95p

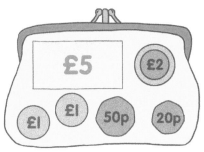

£5    £2
£1    £1    50p    20p

I'll have a sandwich!

I'll pay with (£2) and (£1).

**a** Ella has the pizza.
She pays with [     ]. £5 note and £1 coin

**b** Ella has the apple juice.
She pays with [     ]. 50p and 20p coins

## Teaching sequence

**4**

- Look for pupils who can apply the strategy taught in the earlier sections. They need to count and work out the exact amount of money required to pay for the items.
- Pupils also need to identify the coins or notes used to pay for the items. Note that there may be more than one way of paying.
- Ask pupils to look at the items on the menu. Ask them to tell you how they would pay for the items.
- Work through the example to think of other ways to pay for the sandwich. E.g., using three £1 coins, using six 50p coins.
- Record all the possible ways pupils can think of.
- Group pupils into pairs and ask them to answer the questions. Encourage volunteers to share their answers with the class.

## Thinking skills
- Analysing parts and whole
- Induction

## What you will need
- Three each of 5p, 10p, 20p and 50p coins
- Paper cup

## Independent work
Practice 3 in Practice Book ID, pp 79 to 84.

## Teaching sequence

**5** *Game*
- Ask pupils to work in pairs and to follow the steps to play the game.
- Remind pupils that the total amount of the 3 coins should not be more than £1.
- Once the correct answer has been guessed, ask pupils to swap roles.

---

**Game**

**5** **Money under my cup!**

**Players: 2**
**You will need:**
- 5p, 10p, 20p and 50p coins (three of each)
- a paper cup

How to play:

1 Player 1 hides 3 coins under the cup. They must not add up to more than £1.

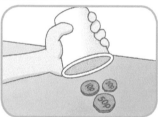

2 Player 1 says how much money is under the cup.

I have 80p.

3 Player 2 guesses which coins are hidden.

3 coins make up 80p. One 50p, one 20p and one 10p?

4 Player 1 checks the answer. Take turns to play. Have 5 turns each.

You're right!

Practice Book ID, p.79

130

**238** **Unit 18:** Money (1)

## Objective of activity: Maths Journal

Pupils will be able to:
- calculate and select the correct statements that match
- calculate the amount in notes and coins

## Objective of activity: Put On Your Thinking Caps!

Pupils will be able to:
- guess and check the notes under a cup that add up to £50
- make a systematic list of the different ways to get £50

## Thinking skills

- Analysing parts and whole
- Induction

## Heuristic for problem solving

Make a systematic list

## Independent work

*Challenging Practice, Problem Solving* and *Maths Journal* in Practice Book ID, pp 85 to 88.

## Teaching sequence

**6** *Maths Journal*
- Use this activity to help pupils summarise some of the concepts and skills they have covered in this unit.
- This is also another way to assess pupils' understanding of the concept of money and counting money.

**7** *Put On Your Thinking Caps!*
- Read the question together and discuss strategies for finding the answer. Ask pupils to work in pairs. Encourage pupils to create a list of all the different ways of making £50 from the notes available.
- When pupils have found the different ways of making £50, help them to rule out the options that involve more or less than 3 notes.
- Ask the pairs to explain their answers.

---

## Maths Journal

**6**  £5 £10  20p  20p  50p

Which of the sentences are correct?

a  There are three 20p coins.

b  There is only one £5 note. ✓

c  I can exchange the coins for nine 10p coins. ✓

d  I can exchange the notes for two £1 coins.

## Put On Your Thinking Caps!

**7**  Miya has 3 notes under a cup.

The notes add up to £50.

They can be £5, £10, £20 or £50 notes.

What are the notes under the cup?

  £20, £20, £10

| Practice Book ID, p.85 | Practice Book ID, p.87 |

131

## Unit 18   Money (I)

Date: _____

**1** How much money is there?
Fill in the boxes.

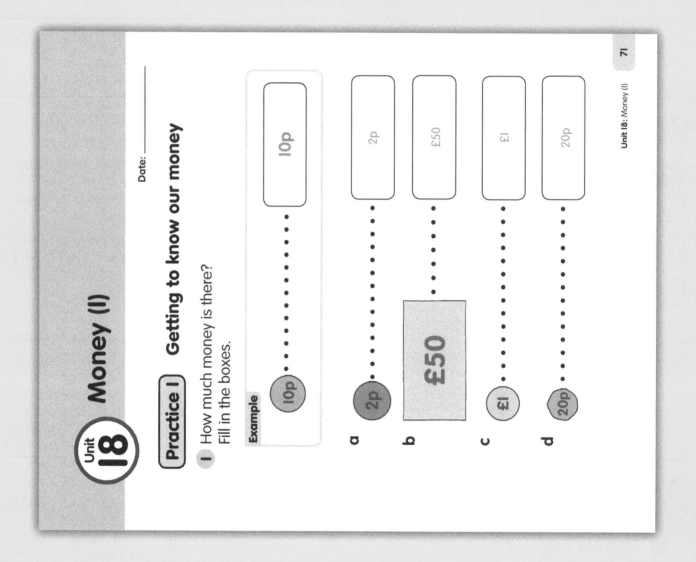

Example

10p ........... 10p

a   2p ........... 2p

b   £50 ........... £50

c   £3 ........... £3

d   20p ........... 20p

2 Write the amount of money in numbers.

| Example | | | |
|---|---|---|---|
| **a** five pence | **5p** | **b** ten pence | 10p |
| **c** two pence | 2p | **d** fifty pence | 50p |
| **e** twenty pence | 20p | **f** one pence | 1p |
| **g** one pound | £1 | **h** two pounds | £2 |
| **i** five pounds | £5 | **j** ten pounds | £10 |

---

**e** £5 .......... £5

**f** £2 .......... £3

**g** £10 .......... £10

**h** £20 .......... £20

**i** 5p .......... 5p

**j** 50p .......... 50p

**k** 1p .......... 1p

## Practice 2 Exchanging money

1 Fill in the spaces.

a One 5p coin (5p) = _5_ 1p coins

b One 10p coin (10p) = _10_ 1p coins

c One 20p coin (20p) = _20_ 1p coins

d One £1 coin (£1) = _100_ 1p coins

e One 50p coin (50p) = _5_ 10p coins

f One 20p coin (20p) = _4_ 5p coins

g One £1 coin (£1) = _5_ 20p coins

3 Farha has these coins in her purse.

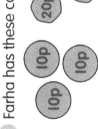      

a How many 10p coins are there? _3_

b How many coins does Farha have altogether? _15_

c How many fewer 10p coins than 5p coins are there? _4_

4 Peter has saved this money.

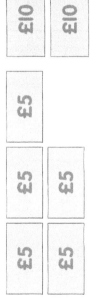

a How many £2 coins does Peter have? _3_

b How many notes does Peter have altogether? _7_

c How many more £5 notes than £10 notes does Peter have? _3_

**2** Fill in the spaces.

**a** One £2 coin **£2**

= __2__ £1 coins

**b** One £10 note **£10**

= __10__ £1 coins

**c** One £5 note **£5**

= __5__ £1 coins

**d** One £10 note **£10**

= __2__ £5 notes

**e** One £20 note **£20**

= __2__ £10 notes

**f** One £50 note **£50**

= __5__ £10 notes

**3** Look at the amount of money on the left.
Colour coins or notes on the right to make the same amount of money.

Answers vary

**a** **50p**

**b** **£1**

**c** **£5**

**d** **£50**

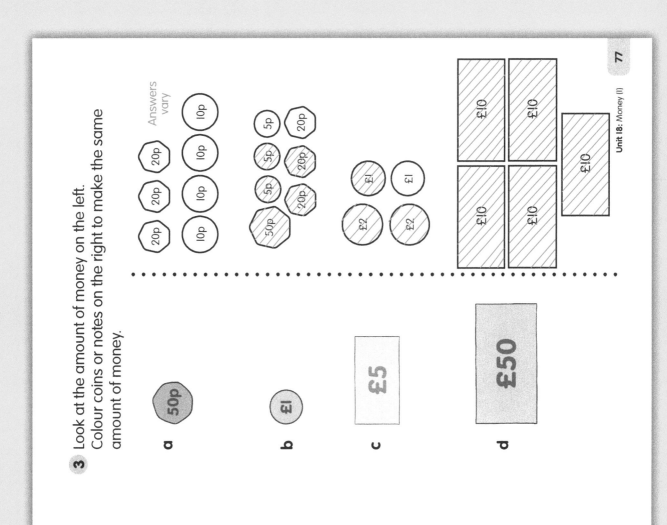

## Practice 3  Work out the amount of money

1  How much money is there?

| |  |  |
|---|---|---|
| a | 50p 20p 20p 20p 5p | 95 p |
| b | 20p 10p 1p 20p 5p 1p | 37 p |
| c | £2 £5 £1 £10 £10 | £ 18 |
| d | £10 £5 £10 £3 £3 | £ 27 |
| e | 50p 50p 50p 50p £1 £1 £1 | £ 4 |

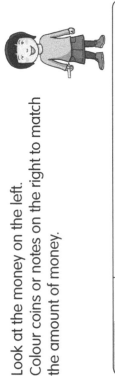

4  Look at the money on the left.
Colour coins or notes on the right to match
the amount of money.

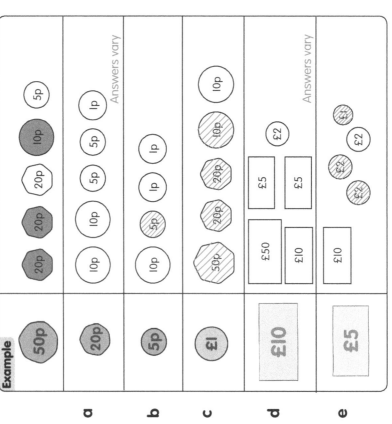

| Example | | |
|---|---|---|
| 50p | 50p 20p 20p 20p 10p 5p | |
| a | 20p | 10p 10p 5p 5p 5p 1p  — Answers vary |
| b | 5p | 10p 5p 1p 1p 1p |
| c | £3 | 50p 20p 20p 10p 5p 10p |
| d | £10 | £3 £5 £10 £5 £2  — Answers vary |
| e | £3 | £10 £3 £3 £4 £2 |

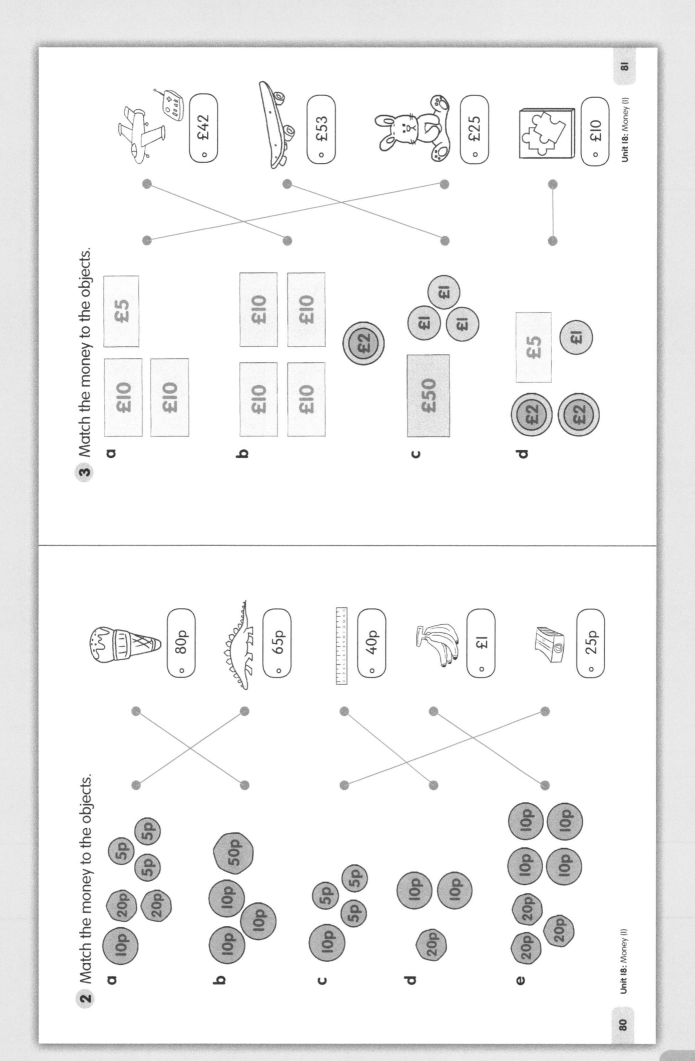

**3** Match the money to the objects.

£42  ○

£53  ○

£25  ○

£10  ○

a  £10  £5
   £10

b  £10  £10
   £10  £10

c  £50  £2
      £1  £1
         £1

d  £2  £5
   £2  £1

**2** Match the money to the objects.

80p  ○

65p  ○

40p  ○

£1  ○

25p  ○

a  10p  20p  5p
   20p  5p  5p

b  10p  50p
   10p  10p

c  10p  5p  5p
      5p  5p

d  20p  10p  10p

e  20p  20p  10p  10p
   20p  20p  10p  10p

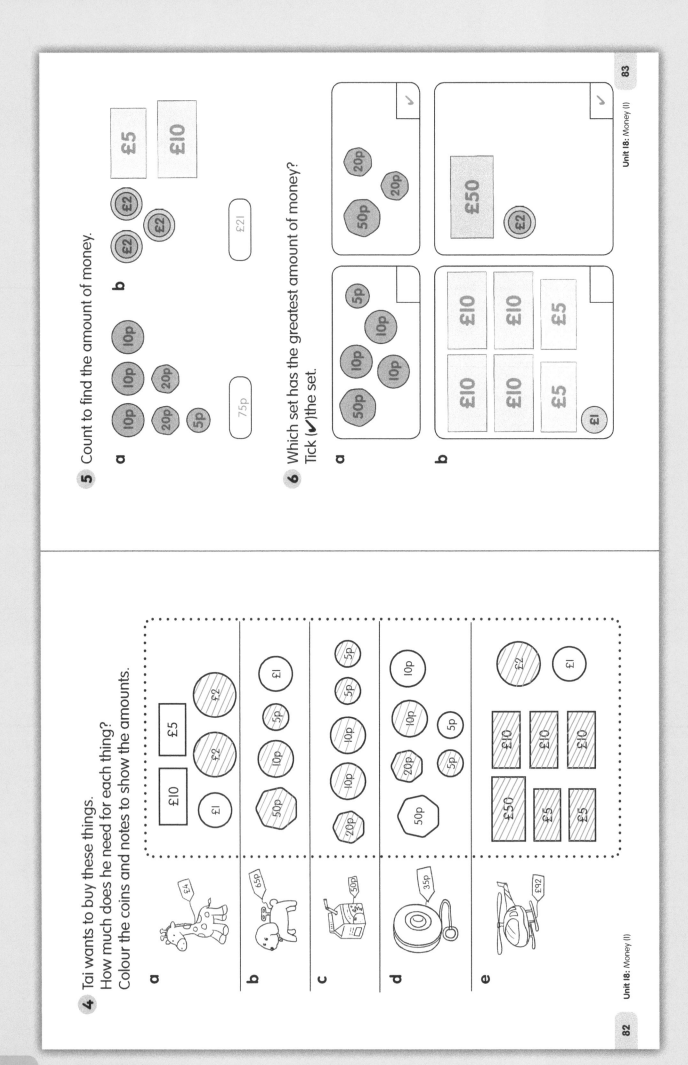

**5** Count to find the amount of money.

a) 10p 10p 20p 20p 10p 5p  → 75p

b) £2 £2 £2 10p 10p £5 £10  → £23

**6** Which set has the greatest amount of money? Tick (✔) the set.

a) 50p 10p 10p 10p 5p  |  50p 20p 20p £50 £2 ✔

b) £10 £10 £10 £10 £5 £5  |  £50 £2 ✔

**4** Tai wants to buy these things.
How much does he need for each thing?
Colour the coins and notes to show the amounts.

a) £3 — £10 £5 £1 £2 £2 50p 5p

b) 65p — £1 50p 10p 10p 5p 5p

c) 50p — 20p 10p 10p 5p 5p

d) 35p — 50p 20p 10p 10p 5p 5p

e) £92 — £50 £10 £10 £10 £5 £5 £2 £1

## Challenging Practice

**1** Ben is going shopping.
Colour coins and notes to show how much money he needs.

| | | |
|---|---|---|
| **a** | 10p 10p 20p / 10p 10p / 20p 20p *Answers vary* | 50p |
| **b** | 50p 10p 20p / 10p 5p / 20p 20p *Answers vary* | 95p |
| **c** | £10 £5 / £3 £2 £2 *Answers vary* | £13 |
| **d** | £5 £2 £2 / £2 £2 / £1 £1 £1 £1 £3 *Answers vary* | £10 |
| **e** | £50 £5 / £10 £10 / £2 £2 £2 £1 £1 | £73 |

---

**7** Count the coins.
Find the amount of money in each set.

**a**

Set A    50p  10p  10p  10p  10p  5p  5p

Set B    20p  20p  20p  20p  20p  20p

The amount in Set __A__ is smaller than the amount in Set __B__.

**b**

Set A    £10  £10  £10  £10  £5    £2  £1

Set B    £50  £10  £13  £13    £2

The amount in Set __B__ is greater than the amount in Set __A__.

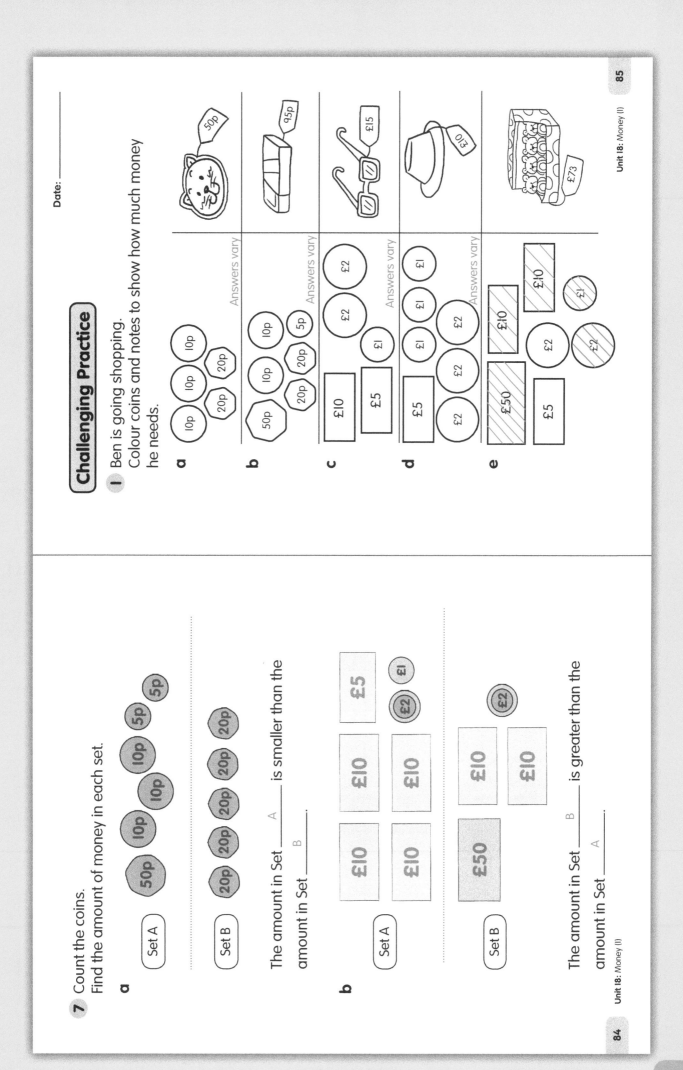

Date: _____

## Problem Solving

**1** Miya wants to buy these glasses of juice.

I am buying drinks for Jack and Ruby.

orange juice 30p

apple juice 20p

orange = 30p

apple = 20p

She uses five coins.
Draw the coins Miya uses.

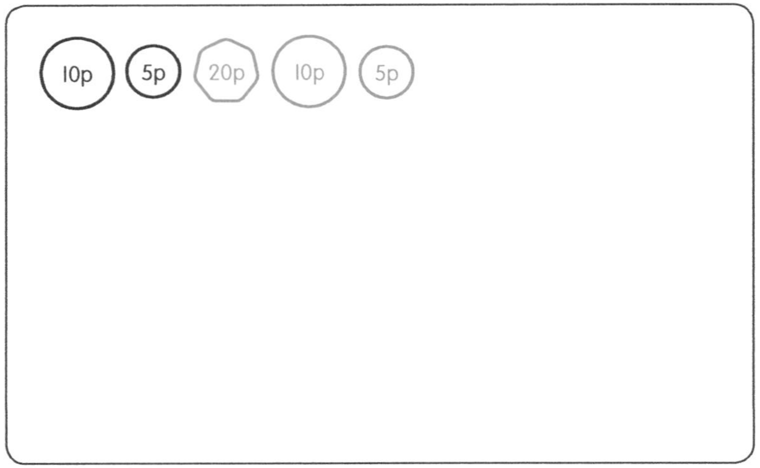

10p  5p  20p  10p  5p

---

**2** Colour the amount shown.

**Example**

£3

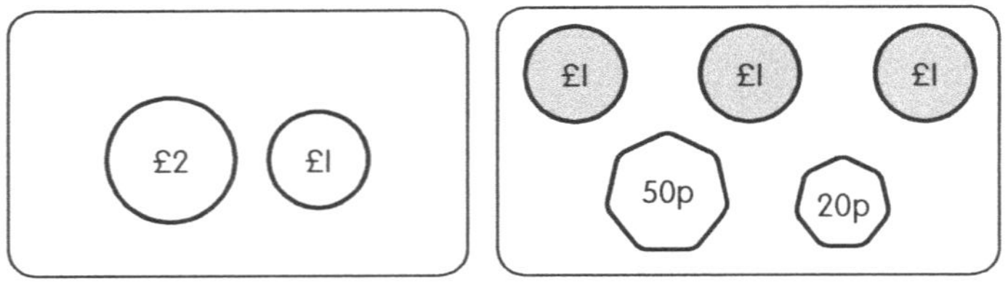

| £2 | £3 |

£3  £3  £3  20p  50p

**a** £5

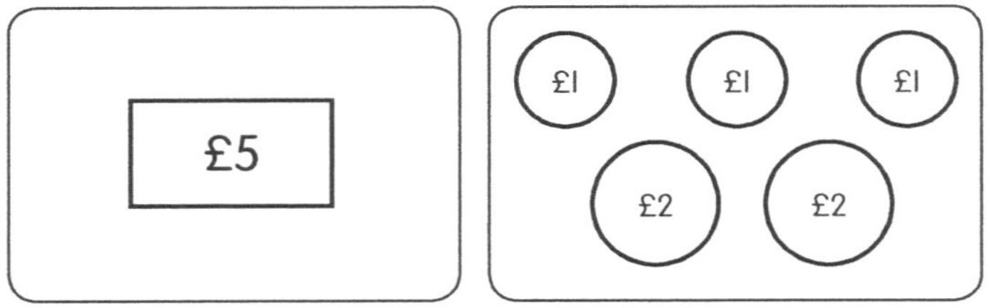

£5

£1  £1  £1  £2  £2

Answers vary

**b** 70p

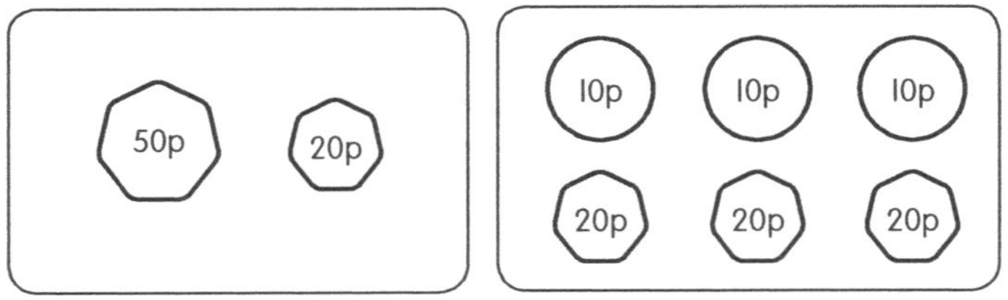

50p  20p

10p  10p  10p  20p  20p  20p

Answers vary

Date: _____

## Maths Journal

Hardeep and Ella put all their money on a table.

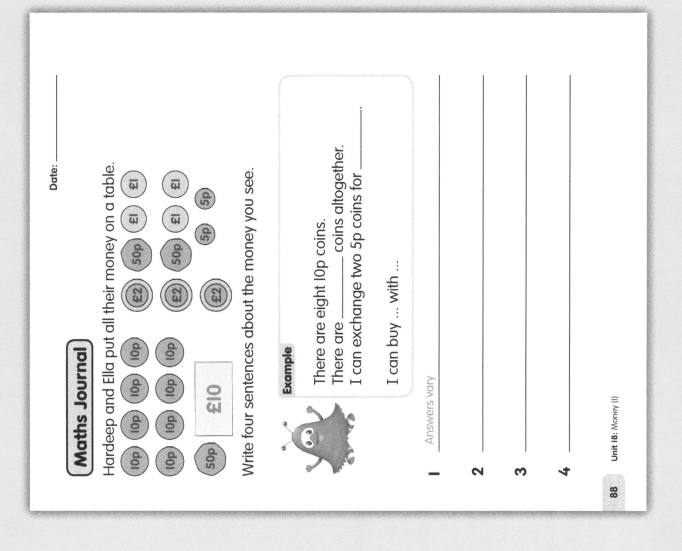

| 10p | 10p | 10p | | £2 | 50p | £1 | £1 |
|---|---|---|---|---|---|---|---|
| 10p | 10p | 10p | | £2 | 50p | £1 | £1 |
| 10p | 10p | | | £2 | | 5p | 5p |
| 10p | 50p | | | | | | |

£10

Write four sentences about the money you see.

**Example**

There are eight 10p coins.

There are _____ coins altogether.

I can exchange two 5p coins for _____.

I can buy … with …

Answers vary

1 _____

2 _____

3 _____

4 _____

Unit 18: Money (I)

# Unit 19: Money (2)

## Medium-term plan

| Week | Learning Objectives | Thinking Skills | Resources |
|---|---|---|---|
| 7 | **(1) Adding and subtracting in pence**<br><br>Pupils will be able to:<br>• state the cost of each item in pence<br>• add to find the cost of two items<br>• subtract to find the change<br>• add and subtract money in pence (up to £1) without regrouping<br>• use number bonds to find the cost of each of the two items that make up a total cost in pence<br>• identify operations used for solving simple word problems | • Analysing parts and whole<br>• Comparing<br>• Applying number bonds | • Pupil Textbook 1B, pp 132 to 135<br>• Practice Book 1D, pp 89 to 96<br>• Teacher's Guide 1B, pp 252 to 255 |
| 7 | **(2) Adding and subtracting in pounds**<br><br>Pupils will be able to:<br>• state the cost of each item in pounds<br>• add to find the cost of two items<br>• subtract to find the difference in cost of the two items, to find the change and to find 'more' or 'less'<br>• use number bonds to find the cost of each of the two items that make up a total cost in pounds<br>• identify operations used for solving simple word problems | • Analysing parts and whole | • Pupil Textbook 1B, pp 136 to 137<br>• Practice Book 1D, pp 97 to 100<br>• Teacher's Guide 1B, pp 256 to 257 |

# Unit 19: Money (2)

| Week | Learning Objectives | Thinking Skills | Resources |
|---|---|---|---|
| 7 – 8 | **(3) Solving word problems**<br><br>Pupils will be able to:<br>• solve word problems on addition and subtraction of money in pence or pounds only<br>• apply addition and subtraction concepts to solve word problems in pence or pounds<br><br>*Let's Explore!*<br><br>Pupils will be able to:<br>• apply the number bond concept to find the individual cost of two items<br>• solve word problems using addition and subtraction of money | • Analysing parts and whole<br>• Comparing<br>• Applying addition and subtraction concepts | • Pupil Textbook IB, pp 138 to 141<br>• Practice Book ID, pp 101 to 104<br>• Teacher's Guide IB, pp 258 to 261 |
| 8 | *Put On Your Thinking Caps!*<br><br>Pupils will be able to make a list of coins that make up a cost in pence. | • Analysing parts and whole<br>• Comparing<br>• Recalling number bonds<br><br>Heuristics for problem solving:<br>• Make a systematic list<br>• Simplify the problem | • Pupil Textbook IB, pp 142 to 143<br>• Practice Book ID, pp 105 to 108<br>• Teacher's Guide IB, pp 262 to 263 |
| | Revision 2 | | • Practice Book ID, pp 109 to 120 |

## Summative assessment opportunities

Assessment Book I, Test 8, pp 101 to 106
For extension, Assessment Book I, Challenging Problems 4, pp 107 to 108
Assessment Book I, Check-up 4, pp 109 to 123

# Money (2)

## Learning objectives: Adding and subtracting in pence

**Pupils will be able to:**

- state the cost of each item in pence
- add to find the cost of two items
- subtract to find the change
- add and subtract money in pence (up to £1) without regrouping

## Teaching sequence

- Revise the addition and subtraction of whole numbers within 100 involving fives and tens and with regrouping.

  Ask pupils to identify the two items and their costs as shown in the textbook. Model the different ways of adding the costs of the two items to find the total cost, then ask pupils to add the costs of the bookmark and the sweets.

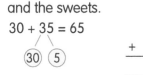

- Next discuss using the strategy of subtraction to find the amount of change.

$$70 - 65 = 5 \qquad \begin{array}{r} 70 \\ -\ 65 \\ \hline 5 \end{array}$$

- Ask pupils to calculate how much change Tai will get after purchasing the two items.

- Ask pupils to recall the number bonds for 80 and identify two items that cost 80p.

- use number bonds to find the cost of each of the two items that make up a total cost in pence
- identify operations used for solving simple word problems

## Key concept

Addition and subtraction concepts in numbers are used in addition and subtraction of money.

## Additional activity

Ask pupils to work in pairs.

Pupil A selects two items from the textbook, and Pupil B adds the cost of both to find the total cost.

Then Pupil B selects one item. Pupil A calculates how much change they would get if they paid for this item with 90p.

Pupils A and B swap roles.

---

### Unit 19 Money (2)

**Let's Learn!**

**Adding and subtracting in pence**

sticker — 60p   bookmark — 30p   banana — 50p   sweets — 35p   balloon — 65p

1. Tai is shopping.

   He has 90p.

   He buys the bookmark and the sweets.

   He has to pay
   30p + 35p = 65p.

   Ella buys a balloon.

   She gives the cashier 70p.

   She will get back
   70p − 65p = 5p

2. You have 80p.
   Which two things can you buy?

   bookmark and banana
   bookmark and sweets

 **Home Maths** Shopping is a good opportunity to help your child learn about money. Ask them to look at price labels and decide which notes or coins to use.

132

**Thinking skills**
- Analysing parts and whole
- Comparing
- Applying number bonds

**Additional activity**

Ask pupils to work in groups of four.

Encourage two pupils to create questions similar to **a**, **b** and **c**. Then ask the other two pupils to solve the questions.

Ask pupils to swap roles and repeat the activity.

Money (2) **Unit 19**

**3** Here are some things for sale.

bubbles
45p

teddy bear
70p

ball
50p

toy car
65p

toy horse
25p

a bag of marbles
30p

toy frog
80p

a bag of shells
35p

plastic flower
20p

**a** Abby buys a toy car and a bag of marbles.
How much does she spend? 95p

**b** You have 60p to buy two things.
What can you buy? Answers vary

**c** George buys a toy frog.
He pays with two 50p coins.
How much change does he get? 20p

133

**Teaching sequence**

③

- Use this activity to reinforce pupils' understanding and skills in adding and subtracting money in pence.

**a**

- Encourage pupils to add mentally if possible. Point out that they can use column addition or number bonds if necessary.

**b**

- One strategy pupils can use is to make a list of number bonds up to 60 in tens and fives. Then check the list of items to find the answers.
  E.g. 60 = 35 + 25
  From the list of items, pupils can buy a toy horse and a bag of shells.

**c**

- Remind pupils that they can use number bonds to find the answer.

## What you will need
- Dice
- 3 counters
- Play money – twenty each of 5p and 10p coins (see Photocopy master 7 on page 290)

## Teaching sequence

**4** *Game*
- Ask pupils to work in groups of three. Model how to play the game.
- Remind pupils that they may take, pay or exchange money from 'The Bank' or with one another.

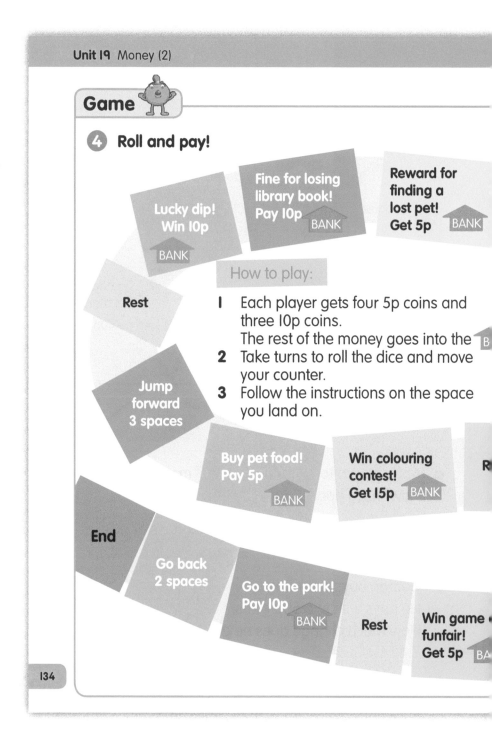

**Unit 19** Money (2)

**Game**

**4 Roll and pay!**

Lucky dip! Win 10p — BANK

Fine for losing library book! Pay 10p — BANK

Reward for finding a lost pet! Get 5p — BANK

Rest

**How to play:**

1 Each player gets four 5p coins and three 10p coins. The rest of the money goes into the B
2 Take turns to roll the dice and move your counter.
3 Follow the instructions on the space you land on.

Jump forward 3 spaces

Buy pet food! Pay 5p — BANK

Win colouring contest! Get 15p — BANK

R

End

Go back 2 spaces

Go to the park! Pay 10p — BANK

Rest

Win game funfair! Get 5p — BA

134

## Independent work

Practice I in Practice Book ID,
pp 89 to 96.

**Start**

Hole in pocket!
Drop 5p

BANK

Jump
forward
4 spaces

Get 5p

BANK

BANK

**4** The game ends when all the players
reach the last space.
**5** Count how much money you have.

The player with the most money wins!

Players: 3
You will need:
- a dice
- 3 counters
- 5p and 10p coins
  (twenty of each)

Get 5p

BANK

Buy everyone
an orange!
Give 5p
to each player.

Present from
a friend!
Get 10p

BANK

Buy stickers!
Pay 5p

BANK

Sell old toys!
Get 5p from
each player.

Miss
a turn

Rest

Practice Book ID, p.89

135

## Learning objectives:
## Adding and subtracting in pounds

**Pupils will be able to:**

- state the cost of each item in pounds
- add to find the cost of two items
- subtract to find the difference in cost of the two items, to find the change and to find 'more' or 'less'
- use number bonds to find the cost of each of the two items that make up a total cost in pounds

## Teaching sequence

- Pupils need to be able to do addition and subtraction of whole numbers within 100 involving one, two, fives and tens and with regrouping.
- Point out to pupils that adding 9 and 11 gives 20.
- Ask pupils to work on the next question which requires subtraction between the two numbers.
- Pupils should relate to their previous experience in comparing and subtracting two numbers.

- Look for pupils who can add and subtract using the concepts in .
- Set up a class post office or bank to give pupils the opportunity to practise adding and subtracting money.

- identify operations used for solving simple word problems

## Key concept

Addition and subtraction concepts in numbers are used in addition and subtraction of money.

## Thinking skill

Analysing parts and whole

---

**Unit 19** Money (2)

## Let's Learn!

### Adding and subtracting in pounds

❶ David buys two toys.

£9 + £11 = £20

He has to pay £20 altogether.

The toy bear costs more than the toy train.

£ [ 11 ] – £ [ 9 ] = £ [ 2 ]

The toy bear costs £ [ 2 ] more.

❷

£40 + £39 = £79

The two hats cost £79 altogether.

The green hat costs less than the red hat.

£ [ 40 ] – £ [ 39 ] = £ [ 1 ]

The green hat costs £ [ 1 ] less than the red hat.

136

**Thinking skill**
Analysing parts and whole

**What you will need**

- At least 4 toys
- Play money (see Photocopy master 7 on page 290)
- Cards for price tags

**Independent work**
Practice 2 in Practice Book ID, pp 97 to 100.

Money (2) **Unit 19**

**Activity**

③ Set up a toy shop.

Add prices to the toys.

Use pounds only.

You have £100 to spend. What will you buy?

How much change will you get?

Practice Book ID, p.97

137

**Teaching sequence**

③

- Ask each group to bring some toys into class.
- Help each group to set up a toy shop using the toys they have brought. Ask pupils to write the prices of their toys on cards (in pounds only) and to place the cards with the toys.
- Each group needs a sales person and a cashier to take the money and count out change. The other members of the group are customers.
- Each customer gets £100. Ask them to visit the shops. Tell them that they can buy any number of toys for £100 or less.
- The cashier adds up the purchases and gives out change.
- Encourage pupils to discuss the items they bought and the change they received.

## Learning objectives: Solving word problems

**Pupils will be able to:**

- solve word problems on addition and subtraction of money in pence or pounds only

- apply addition and subtraction concepts to solve word problem in pence or pounds

## Key concept

The 'part-whole', 'adding on', 'taking away' and 'comparing' concepts in addition and subtraction are used in solving word problems.

## Teaching sequence

- Discuss the different operations of addition and subtraction in **a** to **d**, emphasising and highlighting the underlying concepts in each problem as follows:

**a**

- Use the 'part-whole' concept involving 2 terms in addition. Given all the 3 parts, pupils need to find the whole. The parts are the costs of items.

**b**

- Use the 'part-whole' concept involving 2 terms in subtraction. Given the whole and one of the two parts, pupils need to find one of the other parts. The parts are the cost of item and the change.

**c**

- Use the same concept as **b** in subtraction but the parts vary.

- Ask pupils to explain the parts in this subtraction model.

**d**

- Use the same concept as **a** in addition but the parts vary.

- Ask pupils to explain the parts in this addition model.

---

**Unit 19** Money (2)

**Let's Learn!**

### Solving word problems

Stickers

85p A   95p B   60p C

Toys

£8 D   E £5   F £7

**a** Jack buys all three toys.

£8 + £7 + £5 = £20

He spends £20 altogether.

**b** Miya buys Sticker A.

She pays with two 50p coins.

100p − 85p = 15p

She gets 15p as change.

 50p 50p = 100p

**c** Millie has 70p.

She wants to buy Sticker B.

95p − 70p = 25p

She needs 25p more.

**d** Peter buys toys E and F.

He has £4 left.

£7 + £5 + £4 = £16

He has £16 at first.

## Thinking skills
- Analysing parts and whole
- Comparing
- Applying addition and subtraction concepts

## Independent work
Practice 3 in Practice Book ID, pp 101 to 104.

£45

£37

trampoline                    scooter

**a**  Farha buys the trampoline and the scooter.
How much does she spend altogether?

£ 45  ( + ) £ 37 = £ 82

Farha spends £ 82 altogether.

**b**  Omar buys the scooter.
He pays with £50.
How much change does Omar get?

£ 50  ( – ) £ 37 = £ 13

Omar gets £ 13 change.

**c**  Tai buys the trampoline.
Ella buys the scooter.
How much less does Ella spend than Tai?

Ella spends £ 8 less than Tai.

**d**  After buying the scooter, Ruby has £8 left.
How much does Ruby have at first?

Ruby has £ 45 at first.

Practice Book ID, p.101

139

## Teaching sequence

- Assess pupils' understanding on the use of the addition and subtraction concepts they have learnt in ❶.

**a**
- Use the addition 'part-whole' concept as covered in ❶ **a**.

**b**
- Use the subtraction 'part-whole' concept as covered in ❶ **b**.

**c**
- Use the 'comparing' concept to solve the problem.

**d**
- Use the addition 'part-whole' concept as covered in ❶ **d**.

## Objectives of activity

Pupils will be able to:

- apply the number bond concept to find the individual cost of two items
- solve word problems using addition and subtraction of money

## Thinking skills

- Analysing parts and whole
- Comparing

## Teaching sequence

**3** *Let's Explore!*

- Ask pupils to work in groups to explore the possible answers to each question.

Additional activity
Encourage pupils to say or write
their own word problems based
on the items and prices.

## Teaching sequence

Money (2) **Unit 19**

**Let's Explore!**

**a** Millie has 70p.

What two items can she buy? grapes and toy spider
marbles and toy spider

**b** Omar has £10.

He wants to buy a toy.

After buying the toy, he will still have £5 left.

What toy does he want to buy?  toy boat

**c** Ruby, Jack and Ella want to buy a present for Millie.

Ruby has £1, Jack has £4 and Ella has £2.

Can they buy the bear for her? No.

How did you find out? They have £7 altogether.
The bear costs £9.
They need another £2.

**d** Jack has £60.

He wants to buy a toy.

Which toys cost more money than he has? toy train and scooter

How much more money does he need for each toy?
£40 for the toy train, £1 for the scooter

**e** Ella has five 20p coins.

She wants to buy her brother two things.

Which two things can she buy?

How much does she spend on each thing?
marbles and toy spider, 55p     sweets and toy spider, £1
grapes and marbles, 85p         grapes and toy spider, 70p

141

**a**

- This question is related to the number bond for 70.
- Pupils need to select 2 items which add up to 70p.
  E.g. The grapes which cost 50p and the toy spider which costs 20p.

**b**

- This question involves subtraction. The only possible item that costs £5 is the toy boat. You could extend this problem by asking pupils to identify other toys that Omar can buy with the £5 left.

**c**

- This question involves addition and subtraction.

**d**

- Pupils will need to find the items that cost more than £60. This question involves comparing numbers.

**e**

- Pupils need to explore all combinations that make up £1.

Objective of activity

Pupils will be able to make a list of coins that make up a cost in pence.

Heuristics for problem solving

- Make a systematic list
- Simplify the problem

Thinking skill

- Analysing parts and whole
- Comparing
- Recalling number bonds

## Teaching sequence

**4** *Put On Your Thinking Caps!*

**a**

- Ask pupils to think of 3 ways of getting 85p using 5p, 10p, 20p and 50p.

**b**

- Peter has to buy fruit for 3 people. Remind pupils that each person gets two different types of fruit.
- The total cost should not be more than £40. Ask pupils to work out what he will buy and the amount of change he will receive, if any.

---

**Unit 19** Money (2)

# Put On Your Thinking Caps!

**4** **a**

A pencil case costs 85p.

Miya has some 5p, 10p, 20p and 50p coins.

Show 3 ways that she can use her coins to buy the pencil case. Answers vary

What is the smallest number of coins she can use to buy the pencil case? 4 coins

**b** Peter goes to the supermarket.

He has £40 to buy fruit for Farha, Jack and himself.

He buys two different types of fruit for each person.

What will Peter buy?

How much will he have left?

Help him to choose. Answers vary

142

**Independent work**

*Challenging Practice, Problem Solving* and Revision 2 in Practice Book ID, pp 105 to 120.

Money (2)  **Unit 19**

apples £1

bananas £3

apricots £5

melons £2

oranges £1

strawberries £4

blueberries £4

cherries £6

Practice Book ID, p.105

Practice Book ID, p.108

143

**Teaching sequence**

- For pupils who need additional support, help them to make a list or a table such as the one below to record the details of each person, fruit chosen, the total cost and amount of change.

|  | Peter | | Farha | | Jack | |
|---|---|---|---|---|---|---|
| **Fruit** | | | | | | |
| **Cost** | | | | | | |
| **Total cost** | | | | | | |
| **Change** | | | | | | |

# Unit 19   Money (2)

Date: _____

## Practice 1   Adding and subtracting in pence

1   Add the amounts.

**Example**

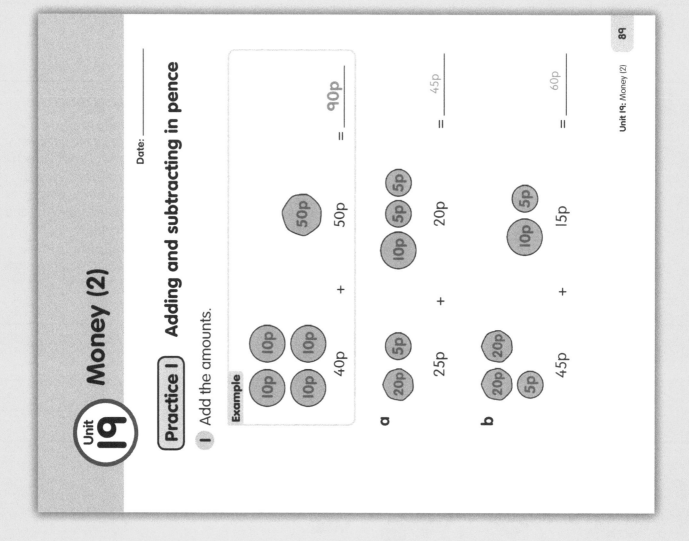

40p    +    50p    =    __90p__

a    25p    +    20p    =    _45p_

b    45p    +    15p    =    _60p_

c  20p to [5p] [5p] [5p] [5p] [5p]

   25p  +  20p  =  45p

d  Two 10ps to [50p]

   50p  +  20p  =  70p

e  Three 5ps to [50p]  =  65p

f  Two 10ps to [20p] [20p] [20p] [20p]  =  [20p]  =  ___

13

---

c  [10p] [5p]     [10p] [5p]
   15p     +     15p     =  30p

d  [20p] [5p]     [5p] [5p] [5p]
   25p     +     15p     =  40p

**2** Add the amounts.

**Example**

20p to [50p]

50p  +  20p  =  70p

a  10p to [20p] [10p]

   30p  +  10p  =  40p

b  50p to [10p] [10p] [10p] [10p]

   40p  +  50p  =  90p

**3** Some toys are on sale.

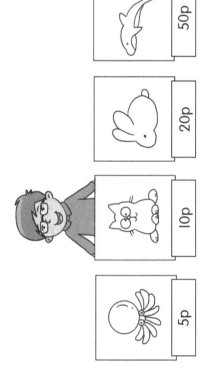

| 5p | 10p | 20p | 50p |

These are the toys the children buy.
How much do they spend?
Fill in the spaces.

**Example**

Peter buys [cat] and [cat] .

20p + 10p = 30p

He spends 30p .

**a** Hardeep buys [rabbit] and [cat] .

20p + 10p = 30p

He spends 30p .

**b** Millie buys [cat] , [ball] and [rabbit] [rabbit] .

10p + 10p + 40p = 60p

She spends 60p .

**c** Ruby buys [fish] , [cat] and [ball] .

50p + 10p + 5p = 65p

She spends 65p .

**d** How much do Hardeep and Peter spend altogether?

They spend 60p altogether.

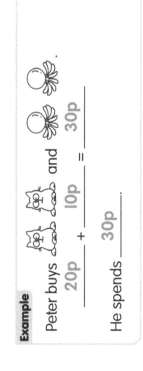

**6** Complete the table.

| You have | You buy | How much change do you get? |
|---|---|---|
| 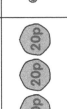 50p | marble 5p | 50p – 5p = 45p |
| 20p 20p 20p |  sandwich 50p | 10p |
| 50p |  toy motorbike 30p | 20p |
| 20p 20p 20p |  whistle 45p | 15p |
| 20p 20p 20p 20p |  kite 60p | 20p |
| 50p |  necklace 40p | 10p |

**4** Subtract the amounts.

a  50p  –  10p  =  40p

b  55p  –  20p  =  35p

c  45p  –  15p  =  30p

d  60p  –  5p  =  55p

e  £1  –  35p  =  65p

**5** Subtract the amounts.

**Example**

50p from 60p

60p  –  50p  =  10p

a  35p from 50p

50p  –  35p  =  15p

b  25p from 70p

70p  –  25p  =  45p

c  60p from 90p

90p  –  60p  =  30p

d  35p from 95p

95p  –  35p  =  60p

**Practice 2**    **Adding and subtracting in pounds**

1. Fill in the missing amounts.

**Example**

| £10 | £10 | £5 | and | £50 |

£25 + £50 = £75

**a** £5   £5   and      (£2 £2 £2)

£6 + £10 = £16

**b** £10   £5   and   £5   £5   £50   £5    (£2)

£15 + £57 = £72

**c** £50   £10   £5   £5   and   £5   £5     (£2 £2)

£60 + £13 = £73

---

7. Jack and Farha buy some fruit.

| apple | orange | banana | pear |
|---|---|---|---|
| 30p | 20p | 50p | 65p |

**a** Jack buys a banana and an orange.
How much does he spend altogether?   __70p__

**b** Jack uses 50p to buy an apple.
How much change does he get?   __20p__

**c** Farha uses two 20p coins to buy an apple.
How much change does she get?   __10p__

**d** Jack buys a pear.
He has 25p left.
How much does he have at first?   __90p__

**e** Farha has two 50p coins.
She buys her fruit and has 70p left.
What does she buy?   __apple__

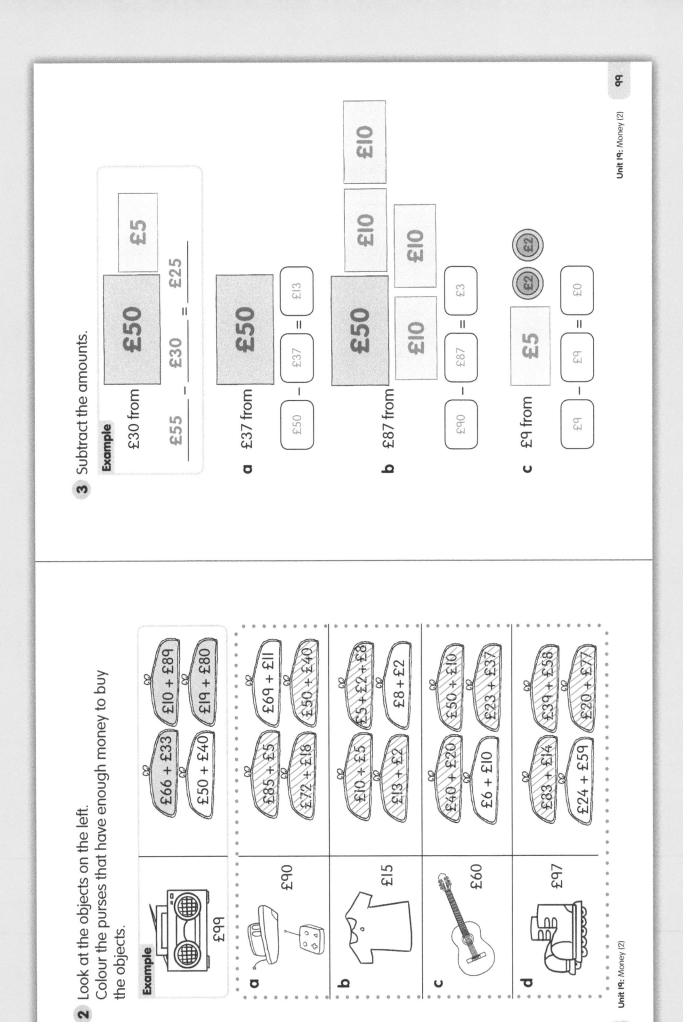

**2** Look at the objects on the left.
Colour the purses that have enough money to buy the objects.

**Example**

£99 (radio)

| £66 + £33 | £10 + £84 |
| £50 + £40 | £14 + £80 |

**a** £90

| £69 + £11 | £50 + £40 |
| £85 + £5 | £72 + £18 |

**b** £13

| £8 + £23 + £53 | £3 + £8 |
| £3 + £10 | £3 + £13 |

**c** £90

| £10 + £50 | £23 + £37 |
| £40 + £20 | £3 + £9 |

**d** £97

| £20 + £70 | £33 + £49 |
| £83 + £14 | £53 + £24 |

**3** Subtract the amounts.

**Example**

£30 from £50

£55 − £30 = £25    £5

**a** £37 from £50

£50 − £37 = £13

**b** £87 from £53

£93 − £87 = £3

**c** £9 from £5

£9 − £9 = £0

## Practice 3  Solving word problems

Solve these problems.

1. Daniel has £30.
He buys a T-shirt.
How much money does he have left?

   £30 – £26 = £4

   He has £4 ____ left.

2. Mrs Hall buys a camera.
She pays £100.
How much change does she receive?

   £100 – £89 = £11

   She receives £11 ____ change.

3. Mario buys some food.
How much does he pay?

   60p + 35p = 95p

   He pays 95p ____.

---

4. The children spend some of the money they have saved.
Help them work out how much money they have left.

| | Before | They spend | After |
|---|---|---|---|
| a | £80 | £79 | £1 |
| b | £75 | £49 | £26 |
| c | £13 | £3 | £9 |
| d | £60 | £22 | £38 |

e  How much more does [ ] spend than [ ]?  £30

f  How much less does [ ] spend than [ ]?  £42

Unit 19: Money (2)

**c** Sarah buys a banana.
She pays with 80p.
How much change does she get?

80p − 55p = 25p

She gets ___25p___ change.

**d** After buying a bicycle, Ravi has £11 left.
How much does he have at first?

£89 + £11 = £100

He has ___£100___ at first.

**e** Andrew buys a racket.
Eve buys a toy car.
How much less does Andrew spend than Eve?

£17 − £5 = £12

Andrew spends ___£12___ less than Eve.

**f** Hannah has £32.
She wants to buy a bicycle.
How much more does she need?

£89 − £32 = £57

Hannah needs ___£57___ more.

---

**4** It's shopping time!

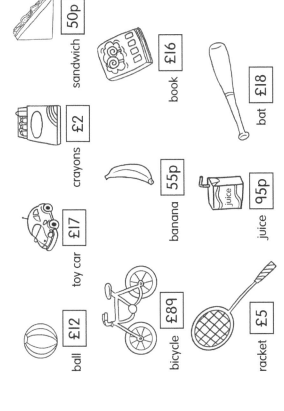

ball £12    toy car £17    crayons £2    sandwich 50p

bicycle £89    banana 55p    book £16

racket £5    juice 95p    bat £18

**a** Nick buys a racket and a toy car.
How much does he spend altogether?

£5 + £17 = £22

Nick spends ___£22___ altogether.

**b** Harry buys 2 sandwiches.
How much does he spend?

50p + 50p = 100p = £1

He spends ___£1___.

**5** How much more is the pencil than the rubber?

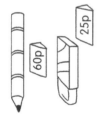 60p     25p

60p – 25p = 35p

The pencil is __35p__ more than the rubber.

**6** Matt has £7.
He wants to buy the book.
How much more does he need?

£23

£23 – £7 = £16

He needs __£16__ more.

**7** George spends £1 on food.
What does he buy?

 banana    sandwich     bun

55p    65p    45p

55p + 45p = 100p = £1

He buys a __banana__ and a __bun__.

---

Date: _____

## Challenging Practice

**1** Do Omar, Miya, Ella and Tai have enough money?
If 'Yes', then work out how much change they will get.
If 'No', find how much more they need.

| | | |
|---|---|---|
| **Example** | pen 65p | ☐ Yes. He will get _____ change. |
| | | ☑ No. He needs __20p__ more. |
| | 40p | ☑ Yes. She will get __10p__ change. |
| | | ☐ No. She needs _____ more. |
| | £12 | ☑ Yes. She will get __£38__ change. |
| | | ☐ No. She needs _____ more. |
| | globe £36 | ☐ Yes. He will get _____ change. |
| | | ☑ No. He needs __£13__ more. |

Solve these word problems.
Fill in the amounts in the purses.

**3** I have £62.
I give £15 to my brother.
How much do I have left?  £47

**4** I have £40.
I have £28 left after buying a toy.
How much do I pay for the toy?  £12

**5** My dad gives me £20.
My grandma gives me £10.
How much do they give me altogether?  £30

**6** Tai has £90.
He buys some games for £55.
How much does Tai have left? £35

**7** Millie has £23.
She gets £15 for her birthday.
How much does Millie have now?  £38

**2** Googol has a lucky day!
Read his story and fill in the amount in his purse.

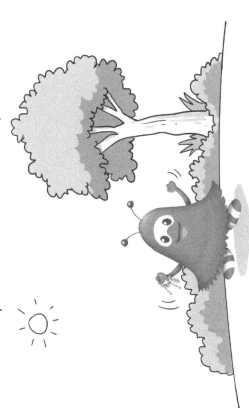

In the morning he goes for a walk.
He has £12 in his purse.

He finds some keys in the park.
He takes the keys to the police station.
They give him a reward of £50.

 £12

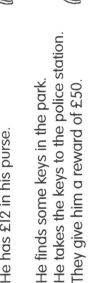 £62

£12 + £50 = £62

## Problem Solving

Date: _____

**1** Bella has less than £1.
After buying a pen, she has 25p left.
Which pen does she buy?

60p
80p

60p + 25p = 85p
85p is less than £1.
She buys the 60p pen.

**2** Mr Brook has more than £70 but less than £100.
He buys one of the pets.
He has £12 left.
Which pet does he buy?

dog    cat    rabbit

£89    £63    £48

£12 + £63 = £75
£75 is more than £70 but less than £100.
He buys the £63 pet cat.

---

# Revision 2

Date: _____

## Section A
**Choose the correct answer.
Write its letter in the box.**

**1** 65 comes just before _____.

a 55      b 64

c 66      d 75

[ c ]

**2**

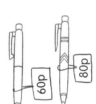

3 tens and 8 ones is the same as _____.

a 8      b 11

c 38      d 83

[ c ]

**3** Look at the number pattern.
What comes next?

34, 37, 40, _____

a 31      b 41

c 43      d 50

[ c ]

**4** 10 more than 65 is _____.

   **a** 55     **b** 56
   **c** 66     **d** 75

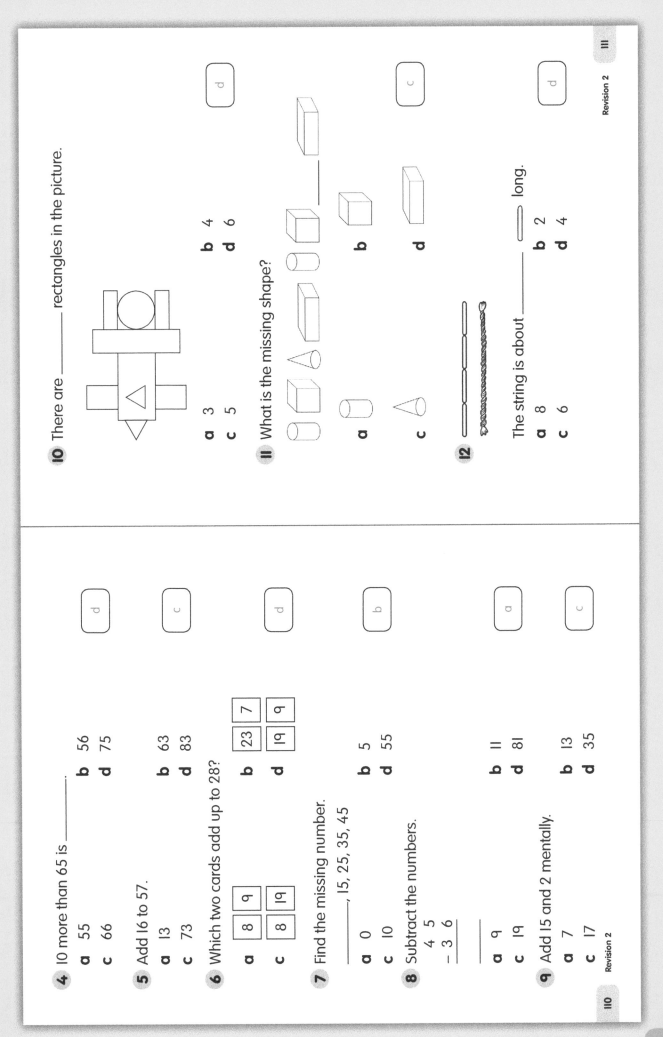

   d

**5** Add 16 to 57.

   **a** 13     **b** 63
   **c** 73     **d** 83

   c

**6** Which two cards add up to 28?

   | 8 | 9 | | 23 | 7 |
   | 8 | 19 | | 19 | 9 |

   **a** 8 9     **b** 23 7
   **c** 8 19   **d** 19 9

   d

**7** Find the missing number.

   _____, 15, 25, 35, 45

   **a** 0     **b** 5
   **c** 10    **d** 55

   b

**8** Subtract the numbers.

     4 5
  – 3 6

   **a** 9     **b** 11
   **c** 19    **d** 81

   a

**9** Add 15 and 2 mentally.

   **a** 7     **b** 13
   **c** 17    **d** 35

   c

**10** There are _____ rectangles in the picture.

   **a** 3     **b** 4
   **c** 5     **d** 6

   d

**11** What is the missing shape?

   **a**     **b**
   **c**     **d**

   c

**12** The string is about _____ long.

   **a** 8     **b** 2
   **c** 6     **d** 4

   d

**13** Which is the longest?

pencil

string

pin

pen

a pen     b string

c pin     d pencil

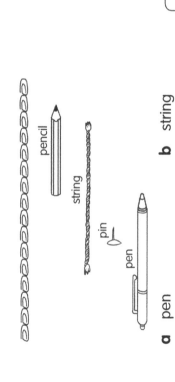    b

**14** Look at the pictures.

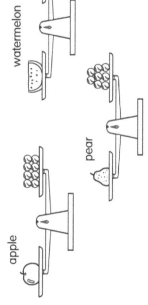

apple

pear

watermelon

Which statement is correct?

a The pear is heavier than the watermelon.

b The watermelon is lighter than the apple.

c The mass of the pear is 1 ⊘ more than the mass of the apple.

d The apple is 2 ⊘ lighter than the watermelon.

d

**15** Look at the picture graph.
It shows the number of stickers Farha, Peter, Hardeep and Jack have.

| Farha | | | | | | | | | |
| Peter | | | | | | | | | |
| Hardeep | | | | | | |
| Jack | | | | | | | | |

Each ☐ stands for 1 sticker.

How many stickers do Peter and Jack have altogether?

a 11     b 13

c 19     d 32

c

**16** How many stickers are there?

a 6     b 12

c 24     d 30

d

**17** Complete the addition sentence.

$7 + \boxed{\phantom{0}} = 10$

a 0     b 3

c 10     d 17

b

## Section B
**Read the questions carefully.**
**Work out the answers and write them on the answer lines.**

**21**  11 + 8 = _____ 19

**22**  Look at the picture.
Write the number in words.

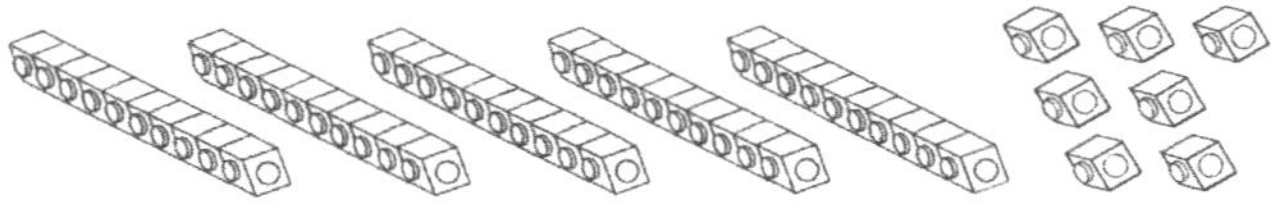

fifty-seven

**23**  Arrange the numbers in order.
Begin with the smallest.

| 75 | 41 | 18 | 29 |

18 , 29 , 41 , 75

smallest

**24**  Add the 2nd and the 5th numbers below.

37   20   19   62   45   83   51

1st

65

---

**18**  What time does the clock show?

a   6 o'clock        b   half past 6

c   7 o'clock        d   half past 7

[ d ]

**19**  How much is there here?

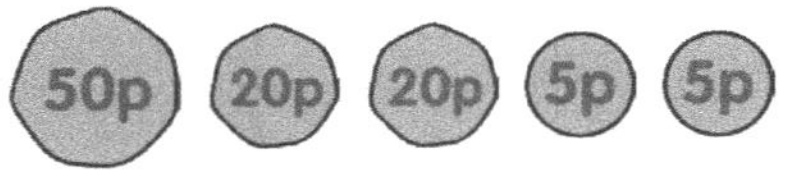

50p  20p  20p  5p  5p

a   95p        b   75p

c   £1         d   5p

[ c ]

**20**  Four children want to buy this toy.

£98

I have four
£10 notes.
Ella

I have two
£10 notes.
Ruby

I have two
£2 coins.
Omar

I have two
£50 notes.
Jack

Who has enough money to buy the toy?

a   Jack        b   Omar

c   Ella        d   Ruby

[ a ]

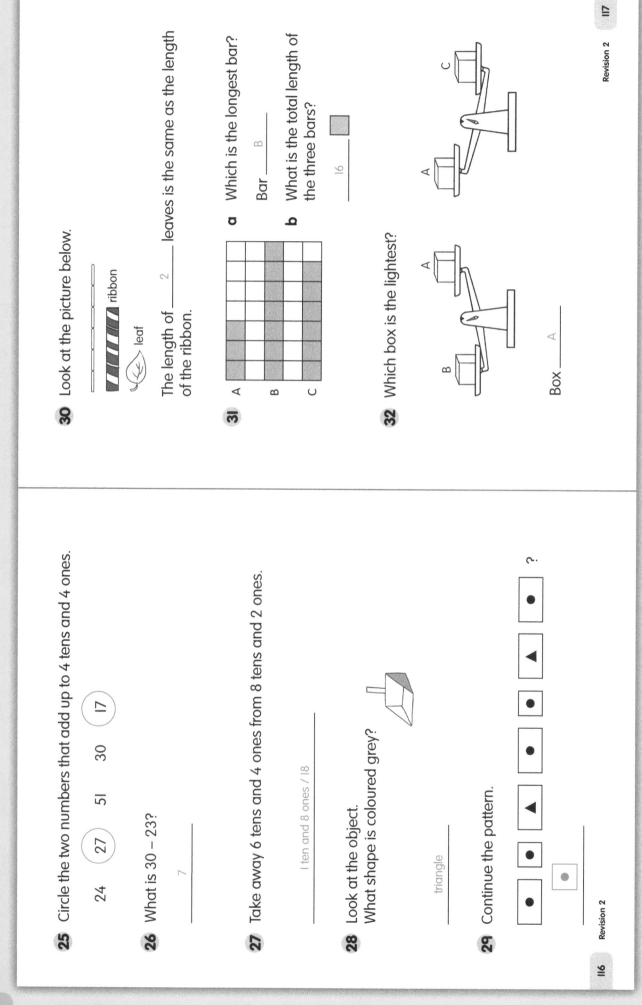

**25** Circle the two numbers that add up to 4 tens and 4 ones.

24 (27) 51 30 (17)

**26** What is 30 – 23?

_7_

**27** Take away 6 tens and 4 ones from 8 tens and 2 ones.

_1 ten and 8 ones / 18_

**28** Look at the object.
What shape is coloured grey?

_triangle_

**29** Continue the pattern.

**30** Look at the picture below.

ribbon

leaf

The length of ___2___ leaves is the same as the length of the ribbon.

**31**
A
B
C

**a** Which is the longest bar?

Bar _B_

**b** What is the total length of the three bars?

_16_

**32** Which box is the lightest?

B A

C

Box _A_

## Section C
**Read the questions carefully.**
**Show all your workings in the spaces provided.**

**36** Miya has 7 toys.
Millie has 9 toys and Peter has 8 toys.
How many toys do they have altogether?

| 7 | + | 9 | + | 8 | = | 24 |

They have ____24____ toys altogether.

**37** There are 90 children in the library.
32 of the children are girls.
How many boys are there in the library?

| 90 | − | 32 | = | 58 |

There are ____58____ boys.

---

**33** A fruit seller puts 14 apples into 2 groups.

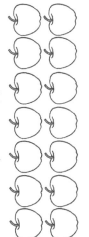

How many apples are there in each group?

____7____

**34** Write the amount of money.

a

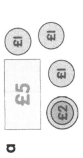

£5  £1  £1  £1  £2

____£10____

b

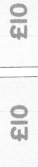

20p  20p  20p  10p  10p  10p  5p

____85p____

**35** Look at the money.

| £10 | £10 | £10 | £13 |

How many £2 coins can I exchange for this amount
of money?

____15____

**38** There are 5 ducks.
Each duck eats 3 worms.
How many worms do the ducks eat altogether?

$$ \boxed{5} \times \boxed{3} = \boxed{15} $$

The ducks eat ___15___ worms altogether.

**39** Farha has 18 stickers.
She puts an equal number of stickers on 3 pages of her
sticker album.
How many stickers does each page have?

| Page 1 | Page 2 | Page 3 |

Each page has ___6___ stickers.

# PHOTOCOPY MASTERS

Noogol

Googol

Koogol

Ooogol

Toogol

Zoogol

# Unit I2: Numbers to 40

Game (Pupil Textbook IB, pp 42 and 52)

| Tens | Ones |
|------|------|
|      |      |

## Unit I3: Mental Calculations

Game (Pupil Textbook IB, p 64)

| | | |
|:---:|:---:|:---:|
| 4 | 5 | 6 |
| 7 | 8 | 9 |

# Unit 13: Mental Calculations

Game (Pupil Textbook 1B, p 68)

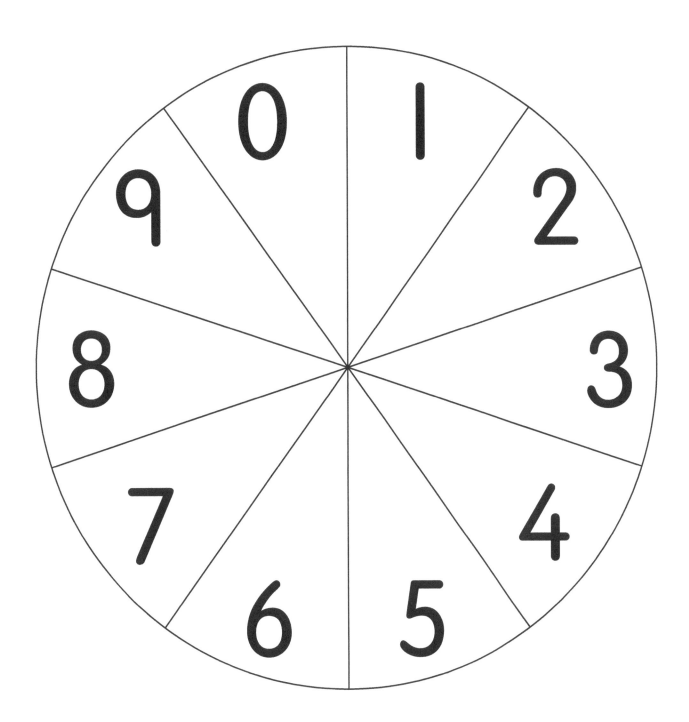

# Unit 13: Mental Calculations

Game (Pupil Textbook IB, p 68)

| | | |
|---|---|---|
| 11 | 12 | 13 |
| 14 | 15 | 16 |
| 17 | 18 | 19 |

## Unit 16: Time

Let's Learn! (Pupil Textbook IB, pp 84, 85 and 86)

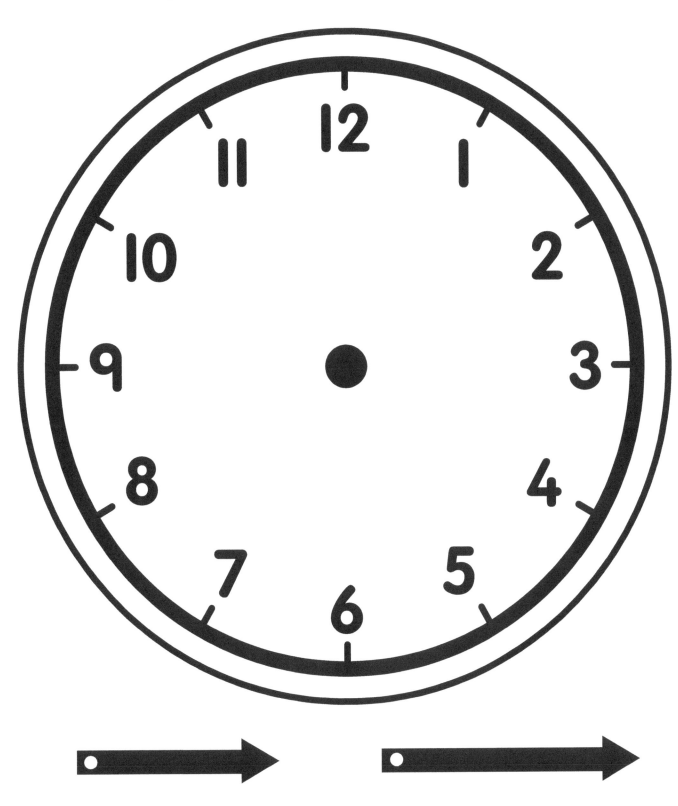

# Unit 17: Numbers to 100

Activity (Pupil Textbook IB, p 96)

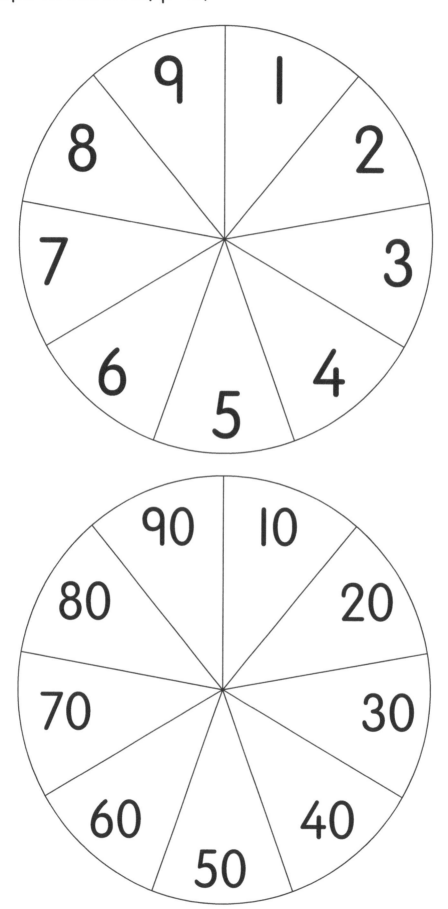

# Unit 17: Numbers to 100

Activity (Pupil Textbook 1B, p 108)

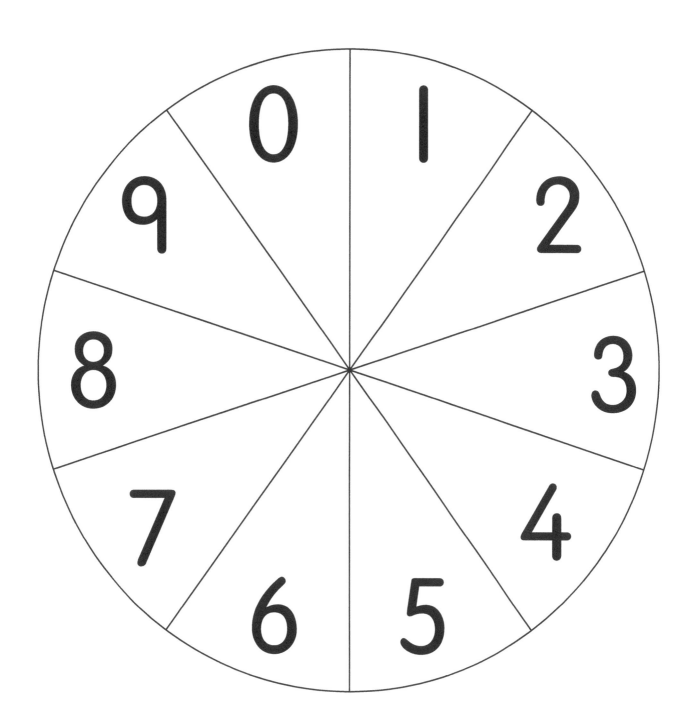

## Unit 18 and 19: Money (1) and Money (2)

(Pupil Textbook 1B, pp 121, 123, 125, 127, 134 and 137)

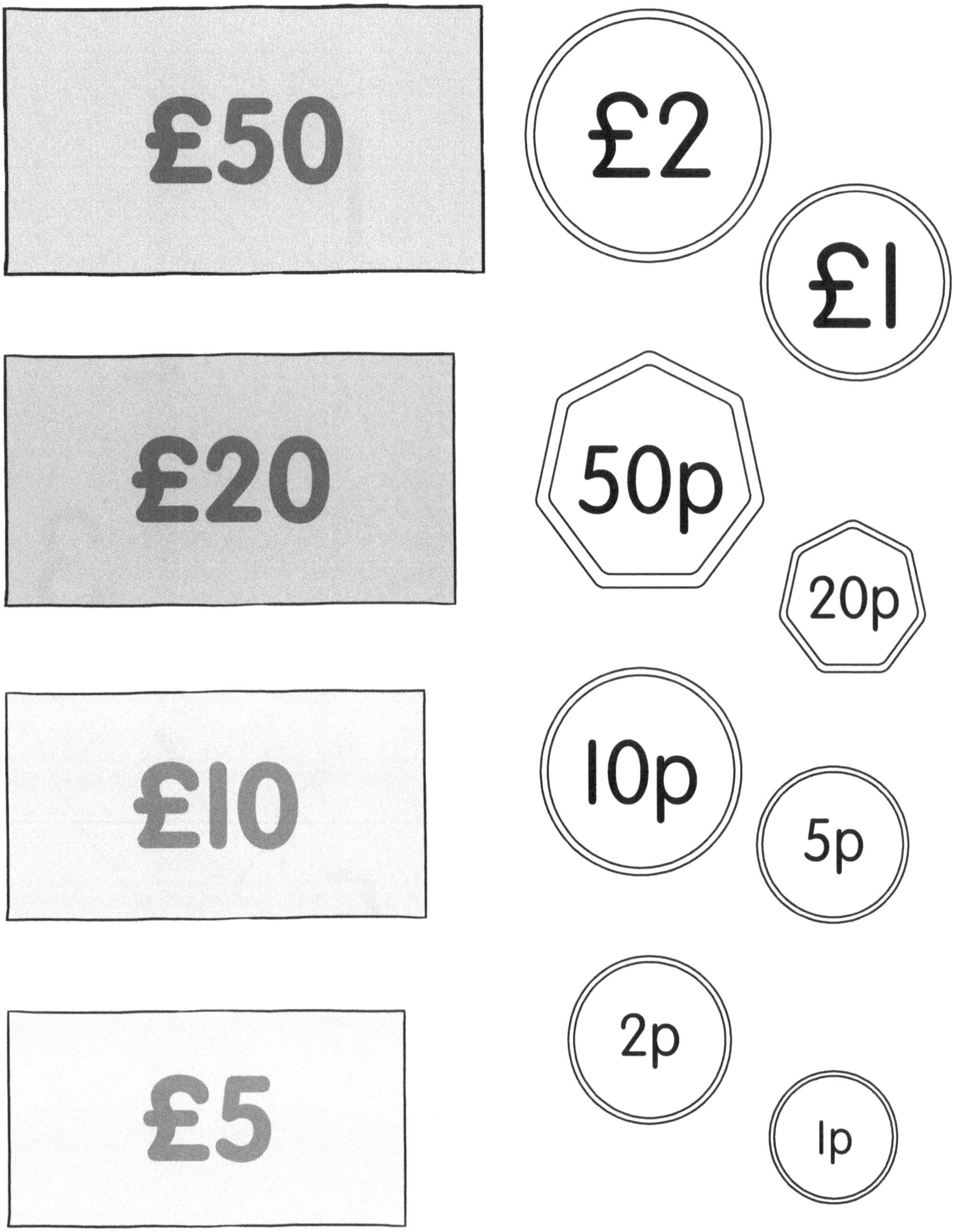

£50

£2

£1

£20

50p

20p

£10

10p

5p

£5

2p

1p